£6.99

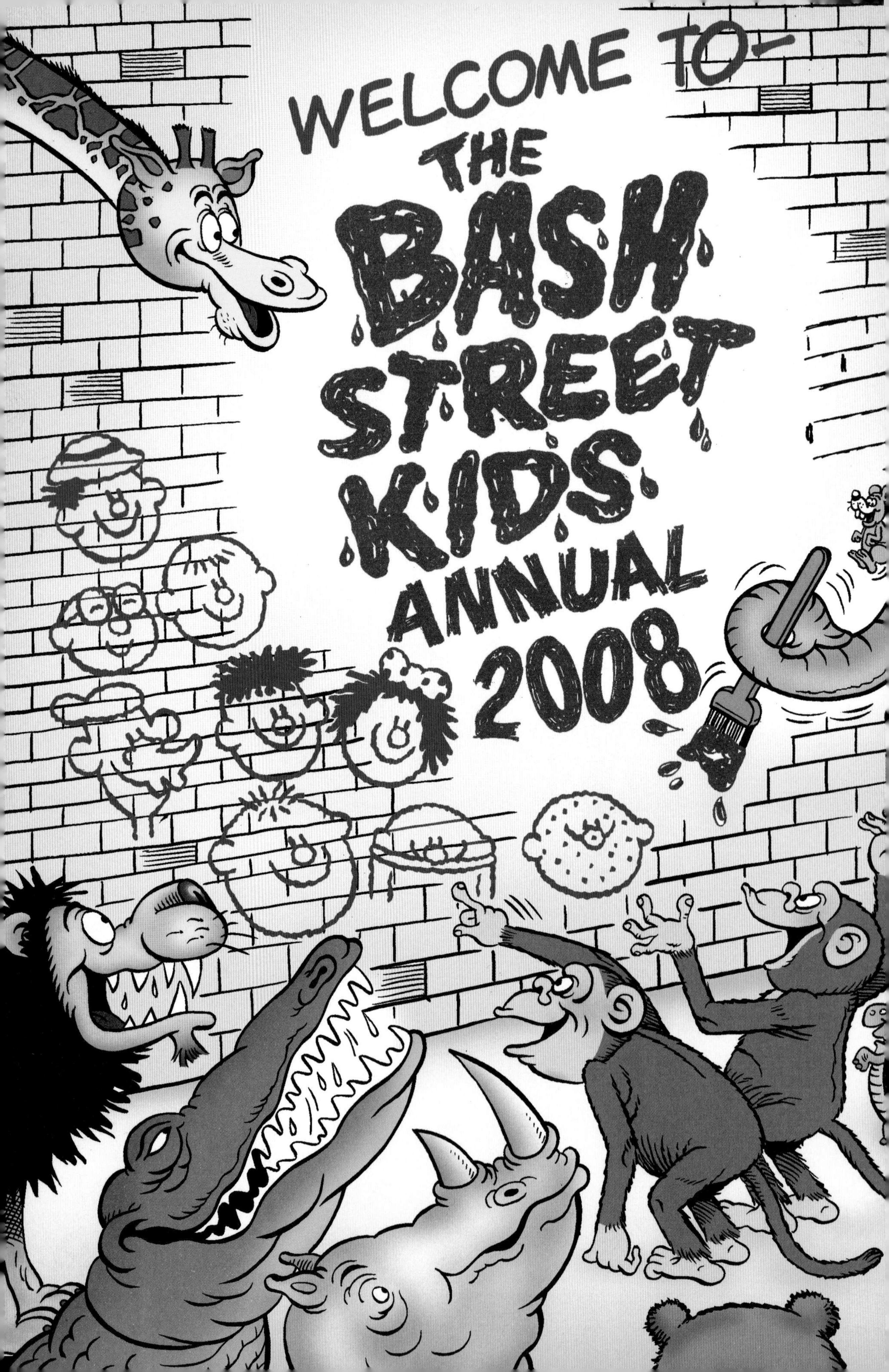
WELCOME TO–
THE BASH STREET KIDS ANNUAL 2008

DS

THOSE ALARMING KIDS
Just after 9.00am-
HMM! SOMETHING'S MISSING!
BUT WHAT?
MY SHOES ARE ON MY HANDS - AS USUAL!
WE'LL SHOW YOU WAYS TO WAKE UP. INTO 'BED WITH YOU!
HEY- BUT...
Suddenly-
HEY! YOU'RE UP TOO EARLY.
YEEEARGH!
I GOT THE SAND FROM THE BEACH.
SO I SEE! HA-HA-HA!
Later-
SCHOOL
I HAVE A PLAN!
NIGEL PARKINSON
At Teacher's house-
MY HERO
IF I TIE STRING TO THE LETTER BOX...
...AND TO MY BIG TOE, THE ARRIVAL OF THE MORNING PAPER WILL WAKE ME UP. BRILLIANT!

MY PLAYTIME SNACK HAS BEEN ORDERED.
MY TROUSERS!! WHEW! THEY'RE THERE!
MY HOMEWORK'S MISSING - NOTHING UNUSUAL THERE!
Then-
I SLEPT IN. MY ALARM CLOCK'S BROKEN.
TEACHER! THAT'S WHAT WAS MISSING!
WITH THIS HANGING OVER YOU YOU WON'T SLEEP IN!
100 LBS
100 LBS
WAAA!
YOU'LL BE FAR TOO SCARED TO SLEEP.
100 LBS
OOOH!
Next-
WITH THIS METHOD, THE WEIGHT OF THE SAND WAKES YOU UP IN THE MORNING.
WAKE UP TO THE GENTLE SOUND OF MUSIC!
IT'S SET TO TURN ITSELF ON.
10:01
OW!
TOOTS DOESN'T DO GENTLE MUSIC!
BOOM-A BOOM BOOM!
Next morning-
TEACHER'S PLAN FAILED...
...THERE'S A NEW PAPER BOY - DAFT SMIFFY!
WHERE DO YOU POST THE PAPERS AGAIN?
DAILY MOAN
GOAL POST

SCIENCE FRICTION
SCHOOL
WE DON'T WANT TO GO TO SCHOOL!
I'M GLAD THEY'RE GOING TO TECHNO'S SCIENCE LESSON FIRST! I NEED A REST!
IT'S A GAME SHOW!
YOU CAN WIN THIS . . .
NORTH POLE TV
. . . SELF CONTAINED IGLOO!
HA-HA!
TURN UP THE POWER AND YOU MAY RECEIVE SIGNALS FROM OTHER PLANETS!
WHAT?
WHAT'S GOING ON?
COME AND SEE THIS, TEACHER!
HUMPH! A SCIENCE FICTION FILM!
WHIRR
SPACE WINDOW
YOU CALLED ME?
WHIRR
COME, O LEADER! FIRST CONTACT WITH EARTH BEINGS!
WHIRR

TECHNO'S OUR SCIENCE TEACHER! HE'S AN ANDROID AND IS GREAT FUN!
SCHOOL
WE LOVE SCIENCE!
EEK!
In Techno's lab.
CAN YOU FIX THIS, TECHNO?
AN ANCIENT RELIC! I MAY HAVE THE KNOWLEDGE IN MY MEMORY BANKS TO REPAIR SUCH AN ANTIQUE!
A SUPER PICTURE NOW, TECHNO!
I HAVE ADDED BITS SO THAT ONE MAY RECEIVE SIGNALS FROM ANY PART OF YOUR WORLD!
LOOK! MONGOLIAN FOOTBALL — LIVE!
WOW! SUPER!
TV PICTURES FROM VENUS. WOULD YOU CARE TO COMMUNICATE WITH THEM?
VENUS TV
YOU MAY SPEAK TO PEOPLE ON VENUS NOW!
PYOING!
PYOING!
BRUSH!
VENUS TV
DUST!
MIRROR
WOW! WE'RE THE FIRST PEOPLE TO SPEAK TO THE BEINGS ON VENUS! COO . . . EE!
GASP!
HUH! SILLY LOOKING BEINGS! VENUS! WHAT RUBBISH! I'VE NEVER SEEN SUCH RIDICULOUS CREATURES!
GASP!
GASP!
I THOUGHT WE WERE THE NAUGHTY ONES AROUND HERE . . .
. . . AT LEAST WE'VE NEVER CREATED A WAR WITH ANOTHER PLANET! NICE GOING, TEACHER!
EH?
LET'S GET 'EM!
SLIDE OPEN
SWOOSH
SWOOSH
LAUNCH INTERSPACE WAR MACHINES! EARTH PEOPLE SHALL PAY FOR THEIR INSULTS!
Don't worry, readers — it'll be 2,000 light years till the armies from Venus arrive here!

Exam Capers
EXAM TODAY
EEK! 39+42–8=73 19X4–2=38
I'M WORKING MY VERY OWN CALCULATOR – CUTHBERT!
GULP! I'VE BEEN CRAMMING TOO MUCH FOR THIS EXAM.
BRAIN FOOD
STUCK
STUCK
YES, FATTY! BUT NOT CRAMMING, AS IN SWOTTING.
WAIL! I NEED MORE PAPER.
TOILET
HERE – USE MINE. I CAN'T THINK OF ANYTHING ELSE TO DO WITH IT.
NOBODY'S GETTING TO SEE MY ANSWERS.
TAP! TAP!

DUH! I KNOW ALL THE ANSWERS BUT I HAVEN'T A CLUE WHAT THE QUESTIONS ARE.
SCRAPE
ANSWERS
HEH! I'VE BROUGHT ALONG MY FURRY PENCIL SHARPENER, CYRIL THE SQUIRREL.
DRRZZ!
I COULD'VE DONE HIS JOB.
DON'T KNOW WHY SIDNEY NEEDS THE WINDOW OPEN. IT'S NOT WARM IN HERE.
SHRIEK! MY BRILLIANT ANSWERS – COME BACK!
GUST OF WIND!
SCOOP
WAHEY! WE LOVE ART EXAMS.
LICK
SPLAT
SPLAT
WE'LL PASS WITH FLYING COLOURS.
SPLOT
BEHAVE! THIS IS GLOSS MISCONDUCT.
DS
SIGH! I WONDERED WHAT WILFRID WOULD MAKE OF HIS BIOLOGY EXAM PAPER.

BUY
BUY
SCHOOL
A bus stops at Bash Street School.
WHAT A QUAINT OLD BUILDING!
SCHOOL
BASH ST SCHOOL
WE MUST SEE INSIDE!
SCHOOL DONATION BOX
£1 COINS ONLY
HMMMMM!
LET'S FOLLOW THAT COIN!
SCHOOL DONATION BOX
£1 COINS ONLY
RUMBLE
THERE IT GOES!
NO EXTRAS FOR US, I'M AFRAID!
RATTLE
RUMBLE
SLOO!
SAY, WHICH WAY TO THE SOUVENIR SHOP, KIDS?
HMM . . . THIS WAY, FOLKS!
Soon —
BRRR! A BIT OF A DRAUGHT! I'LL CLOSE THE WINDOW!
SHIVER
CHATTER
YIKES! WHAT'S GOING ON?
R.I.P
SHIVE
SHAKE
TREMBLE
HO-HO! GREAT SOUVENIRS!
CHUG
CHUG
GASP! MY SCHOOL!
HA-HA! BEST PLAN EVER FOR SOME TIME OFF SCHOOL — GET RID OF THE SCHOOL!

In class.
BLAH . . . BLAH . . .
YAWN
HMM!
BLAH . . .
COO!
GEE, WHIZZ! TAKE A PHOTO OF ME WITH OLD TEACHER!
ERK!
SQUEEZE
CLICK
HO-HO! IT'S TOURIST SEASON AGAIN!
PHUT
CLICK
CLICK
CLICK
CLICK
DO YOU MIND? I'M TRYING TO TEACH HERE!
BZT!
In class.
SCHOOL CRAYONS
SCHOOL PENCILS
TAKE SOME SOUVENIRS — NO CHARGE!
SOUVENIRS — OUR JOTTERS!
PLUG
DANNY
HA-HA! IT'LL SOON BE AN EMPTY ROOM!
TEE-HEE!
SCHOOL
BELL
TUG
GIVE ME BACK MY DOOR!
NO! THIS SUPER SOUVENIR'S GOT TO BE WORTH . . . SAY FIVE POUNDS!
TUG
HEAVE
CHORTLE! THE HEAD'S GOING TO HAVE TO BUY THE SCHOOL BACK, BIT BY BIT! HA-HA!
CHORTLE!
THERE'S ONE SOUVENIR THE HEAD WON'T BE KEEN TO BUY BACK! TEACHER! HA-HA-HA!
I WANT MY SCHOOL BACK!
NO CHANCE!
TEE-HEE!
SNORE! SNORT!

PHONE
and
GAMES
COME ON! COME ON! I'M WAITING!
READER
KIDS NOT ABLE TO ANSWER YOUR QUESTIONS AS USUAL, TEACHER?
IT'S NOT US HE'S TALKING TO — IT'S HIS MOBILE PHONE!
WHAT A SAD MAN! IT LOOKS AS IF HE NEVER GETS A CALL!
So —
EH? I WONDER WHO THAT IS?
DRING!
DRING!
HELLO . . . HELLO . . . HELLO . . .
HA-HA! I'VE CUT OFF THE PHONE JUST AS HEAD PICKED IT UP!
In the Staff Room.
IT'S FOR YOOO-HOO!
SLOO! ME?
OUR BELOVED HEAD
TEA URN
BEANO
SNARL! WHO IS THIS?
IT'S ME! TEACHER!
GRRRR!
STAFF ROOM
OO . . . ER!
WOOZ
THUD! THUD!

YIPPEE! A CALL FOR ME?
HELLO . . . HELLO . . . HELLO . . .
HA-HA! IT'S ONLY THE BELL FOR THE MORNING BREAK!
GOT IT!
WHIRR
WE'LL HAVE FUN WITH IT!
WE'LL GIVE HEAD A CALL — JUST AS HE'S LEAVING THE ROOM!
HUMPH!
GRRR! HELLO . . . HELLO . . .? WHO'S PLAYING TRICKS ON ME?
GRAB
LEAP
HUMPH! THEY'VE RUNG OFF AGAIN!
HA-HA-HA!
CLANG
SLAM
WE'LL LET HIM SPEAK TO THE CALLER THIS TIME! HEH-HEH!
GRRR! AGAIN!
DRING!
DRING! DRING!
WHERE IS HE?
I'LL SOON FIND TEACHER!
SPIN
WELL, AT LEAST TEACHER'S GETTING A CALL!
BREEP! BREEP!
AHA! SOMETHING TELLS ME HE'S IN THAT CUPBOARD!

GARDENING CALENDAR
FROM THE
BASH STREET POTTING SHED
JANUARY — AFTER HEAVY SNOWFALL ALWAYS INSPECT YOUR PLANTS FOR ANY DAMAGE
THIS BUSH HAS GOT DAMAGED — I'LL GIVE IT A PRUNE.
OPEN!
SNIP!
FUME! THAT'S MY TV AERIAL.
FEBRUARY— NOW IS THE TIME TO PUT NETTING OVER YOUR VEG CROPS TO PROTECT THEM FROM HUNGRY BIRDS.
FLAP!
FLAP!
EEK! TOO LATE. THE BIRDS GOT HERE FIRST.
MARCH — BEGIN FEEDING THE GOLDFISH IN YOUR POND AGAIN AS THEY'VE BEEN DORMANT ALL WINTER. REMEMBER — FEED THEM LITTLE AND OFTEN.
SPLASH!
FISH FOOD
SNATCH!
OO-ER! I'VE FED MINE ALL YEAR — LOTS!

PUP PARADE
with the BASH ST. PUPS
BONES
PEEPS
'ENRY
SNIFFY
TUBBY
SPOTTY
MANFRID
WIGGY
PUG
Come on, Pups! Out you get!
NNNGH! We're trying, Bones!
SUDDENLY–
HUH! TOO FAT– THE LOT OF YOU!
POP!
Okay–time to get fit. I'll give you a 'workout'!
DOH!
NNNGH!
One...two...three... keep it moving!
CRUNCH!
FLAP
WHIZZ
WHEEZE!
SOON–
UP! UP! We've got lots of exercises left to do!
DOG TIRED
LATER–
A sprint now. On your marks...get set...
...GO! OH!
ZOOM!
SPLAT!
Thanks, Bones. Your workout got us fitter –
– we're able to run to our food bowls even faster!
Huh! Don't know why I bother!
SLURP!
SLURP!
LAUGH BREEDS
SKY TERRIER

Green Grow the BASH STREET KIDS
OKAY, KIDS! ATTACK THAT COASTAL LITTER AND LET'S SEE WHO CAN COLLECT THE MOST.
I'VE GOT THE MOST!
MEEE!
BOOMPH!
BIFF!
RUBBISH! I HAVE.
DON'T TALK GARBAGE!
GROAN! I SHOULDN'T HAVE USED THE WORD ATTACK!
WE'RE SAVING WATER BY HAVING OUR YEARLY BATH TOGETHER.
SPLASH!
SCRUB!
ROOM FOR A SMALL ONE?
SPLADOOSH
LEAP!
NO! NOT YOU, FATTY.
BANK
FIRST GLASS INTEREST
IN
TIME LOCK
BOTTLE DISPENSER
CLINK
CLINK
BEANOTOWN'S GOT ITS OWN BOTTLE BANK NOW.

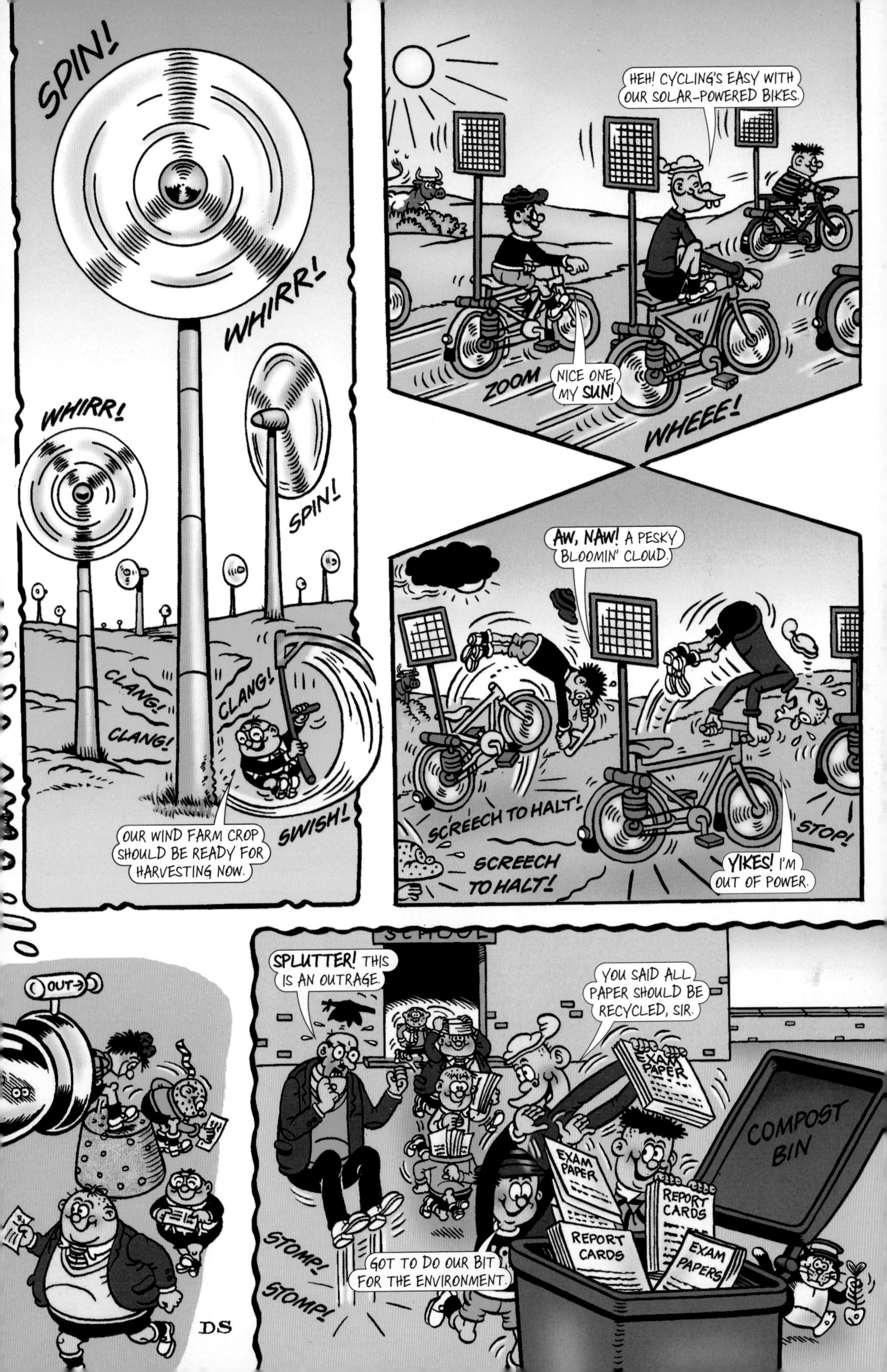
SPIN!
WHIRR!
WHIRR!
SPIN!
CLANG!
CLANG!
CLANG!
SWISH!
OUR WIND FARM CROP SHOULD BE READY FOR HARVESTING NOW.
HEH! CYCLING'S EASY WITH OUR SOLAR-POWERED BIKES.
ZOOM
NICE ONE, MY SUN!
WHEEE!
AW, NAW! A PESKY BLOOMIN' CLOUD.
SCREECH TO HALT!
SCREECH TO HALT!
STOP!
YIKES! I'M OUT OF POWER.
OUT
SPLUTTER! THIS IS AN OUTRAGE.
YOU SAID ALL PAPER SHOULD BE RECYCLED, SIR.
EXAM PAPER
COMPOST BIN
EXAM PAPER
REPORT CARDS
REPORT CARDS
EXAM PAPERS
STOMP!
STOMP!
GOT TO DO OUR BIT FOR THE ENVIRONMENT.
DS

KNIT-WIT TEACHER
YUM!
LOVELY
SLURP!
SMELL
SIZZLE!
GAS
BACK! I WAS LATE THIS MORNING AND MRS TEACHER WAS TOO BUSY KNITTING BOOTEES TO COOK BREAKFAST!
KNIT
SWISH!
SWISH!
BUT DON'T SLEEP TOO LONG — YOU'LL NEED TO GO AND FIND A PART-TIME JOB TO BUY A COT, PRAM, RATTLE . . .
YES!
AND WHEN THE CHILD REACHES SCHOOL AGE . . .
NO . . . NOT . . .
TAP TAP
BASH ST. SCHOOL
HMM!
Later.
WE'VE HAD A GREAT DAY WITHOUT TEACHER!
WE'D BETTER REVIVE TEACHER SO THAT WE CAN ALL GO HOME!
SNIFF! OOOH!
At Teacher's house.
YOU'D BETTER GO HOME AND HEAR THE GOOD NEWS FROM MRS TEACHER!
DOH!
KICK!
ER . . . FINISH THE BOOTEES, DEAR?
YES! THE SECOND SET OF FOUR!

AW! BOOTEES! TEACHER'S GOING TO BE A DADDY!
BURP! BABY?
NUDGE
BABY! I DIDN'T THINK . . . OOH!
SUDDEN SHOCK
FAINT
CATCH
CATCH
BETTER GET SOME SLEEP — YOU'LL NOT GET MUCH ONCE YOUNG TEACHER ARRIVES!
ZZZZ!
PUSH
TUCK
2·00AM
SHAKE
OOH! ZZZ!
TWANG
WATER BOMB
HO-HO! HE'LL LEARN A LOT HERE!
GIBBER!
WHUMP
PING
HAR-HAR!
TRIFLE
SPLUDGE
OO . . . NO ESCAPE! LIKE BEING AT SCHOOL ALL THE TIME!
HA-HA! NO WORK FOR US TODAY!
SWOON
DOH! TOO MUCH TO BEAR!
THUD
FOUR? WHAT KIND OF CHILD NEEDS FOUR?
HA-HA! THEY'RE NOT FOR A BABY . . .
. . . I MADE THEM FOR THE NEIGHBOUR'S DOG! KEEP ITS PAWS WARM IN THE COLD WEATHER! HA-HA! IT'S THE DOG WHICH ISN'T TOO KEEN ON YOU, TEACHER!
GROWL! GRRRR!
ZOOM
WHEEE
THE DOG HAS GOOD TASTE!
HE'LL HAVE A 'GOOD TASTE' IF HE CATCHES TEACHER!

BATTLE
DO
NICELY
Reader.
YOU'D BETTER STOP BEFORE TEACHER ARRIVES!
WOP
OUCH! NO NEED! TEACHER'S BEHIND THIS PUNCH-UP!
ACTION! MORE ACTION!
OOF!
THUMP
BOOT
GASP!
WHEEZ
. . . UP A STEEP HILL OUTSIDE BEANOTOWN!
SQUASH
OO . . . ER! LOOK OUT, MEN!
Then —
EH? FAKE BLOOD? TAKING THINGS A BIT FAR, AREN'T WE? ANYWAY, THE BATTLE HASN'T BEGUN YET!
EH? BURGERS BEFORE BATTLE?
HA-HA! IT'S A PRE-BATTLE SNACK!
SQUIRT
SQUIRT
SPLODGE
SPLODGE
HOI, GENERAL! YOU OWE ME TWENTY QUID FOR YOUR ARMY'S NOSH!
DIAL A BURGER
A FEW SECONDS LATER, THE GENERAL WAS CAUGHT SNEAKING AWAY!
WOW!
TUG
THE GENERAL WAS TAKEN BEFORE A FIRING SQUAD!
ER . . . NOW . . .
PUSH
PUSH
FIRE!
OW! OW! OW!
THUD
PING
POP
POP
THUD
POP
PING
POP
HA-HA-HA!

HORTLE! ENOUGH
TICE! WE'RE GOING TO
A RE-ENACTMENT OF
E 1642 BATTLE OF
EANOTOWN HILL!
YOU CAN TELL THE TALE, TOOTS!
OKAY!
HISTORY OF THE BATTLE OF BEANOTOWN HILL 1642
ONE ARMY WAS LED BY A VERY HANDSOME, BRIGHT, FEARLESS GENERAL . . .
AHEM! I'LL BE THAT GENERAL! SUITS MY OWN CHARACTER!
CHORTLE! DREAMER!
HEH-HEH! SORRY, GENERAL!
SPLOSH
SPLASH
TEACH
. . . THIS TOUGH GENERAL MARCHED HIS TROOPS THROUGH WATER . . .
GASP! ER . . . WELL!
HURRY UP WITH THE TALE, TOOTS!
MUNCH . . . CHOMP! OKAY!
SOON, THE GENERAL HAD HIS ARMY IN POSITION! HE THEN CAST AN EYE OVER HIS TROOPS!
CHINS UP, MEN!
PRANCE
WAH!
POP
POP
POP
POP
POP
AT ELEVEN O'CLOCK — THE BATTLE BEGAN!
DOH!
WOON
HMM! TIME TO RE-ENACT ANOTHER BATTLE, TROOPS!
TWEET
TWEET
OUT COLD
THE BATTLE BETWEEN BEANOTOWN UNITED AND BEANOTOWN CITY LAST WEEK!
THUD
BUMF
BOOT
KICK
KICK

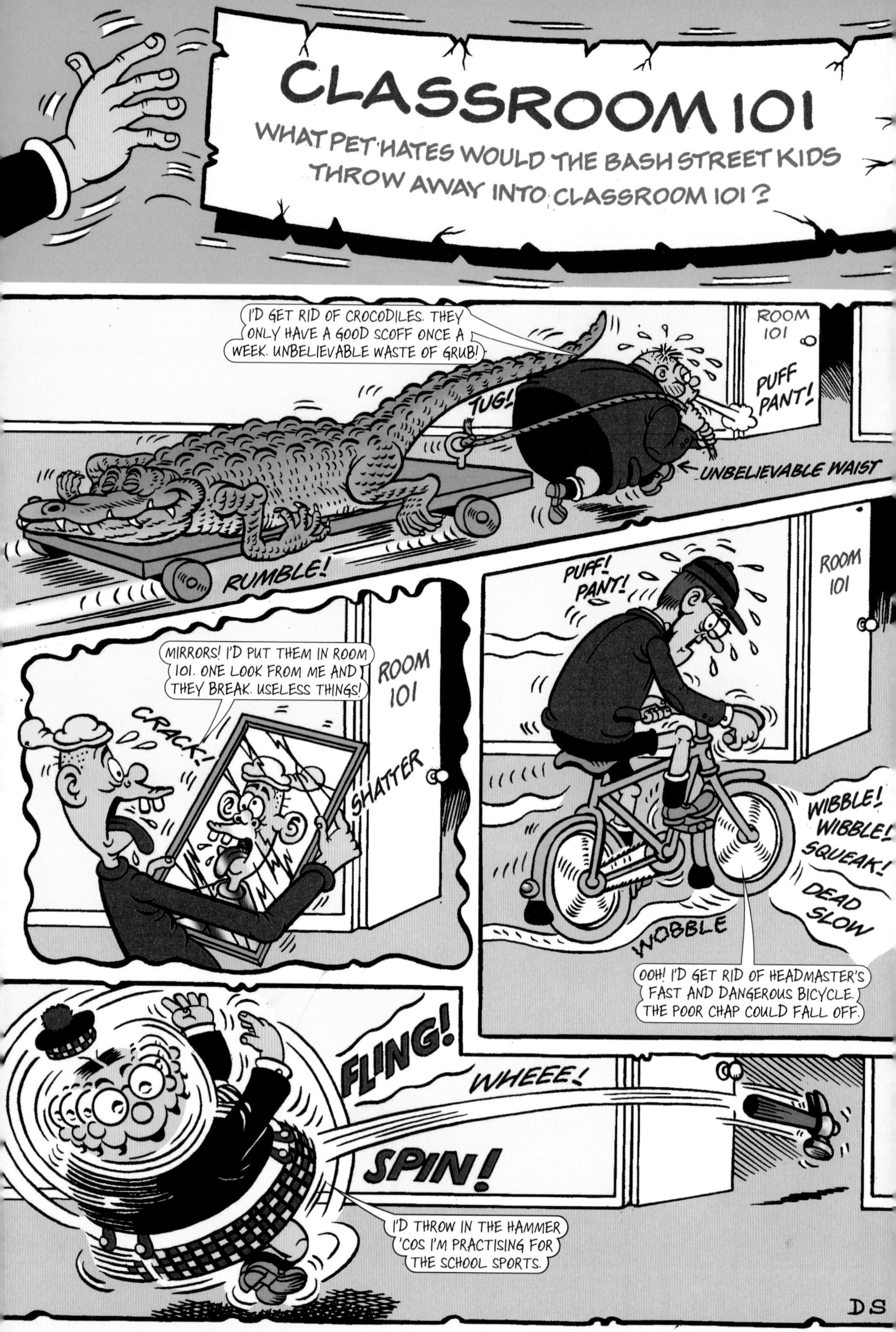
CLASSROOM 101
WHAT PET HATES WOULD THE BASH STREET KIDS THROW AWAY INTO CLASSROOM 101?
I'D GET RID OF CROCODILES. THEY ONLY HAVE A GOOD SCOFF ONCE A WEEK. UNBELIEVABLE WASTE OF GRUB!
ROOM 101
PUFF PANT!
TUG!
UNBELIEVABLE WAIST
RUMBLE!
MIRRORS! I'D PUT THEM IN ROOM 101. ONE LOOK FROM ME AND THEY BREAK. USELESS THINGS!
ROOM 101
CRACK!
SHATTER
PUFF! PANT!
ROOM 101
WIBBLE! WIBBLE! SQUEAK!
DEAD SLOW
WOBBLE
OOH! I'D GET RID OF HEADMASTER'S FAST AND DANGEROUS BICYCLE. THE POOR CHAP COULD FALL OFF.
FLING!
WHEEE!
SPIN!
I'D THROW IN THE HAMMER 'COS I'M PRACTISING FOR THE SCHOOL SPORTS.
DS

TREMBLE
ROOM 101
TROUSERS! MEN ALWAYS GET TO WEAR THEM AND THINK THEY CAN BOSS US GIRLS ABOUT.
TOSS!
CACKLE! I'D THROW IN A STINK BOMB 'COS EVERY ROOM SHOULD HAVE ONE.
ROOM 101
FLING!
GUM BUCKLING GUFF!
ROOM 101
HACKNEY CABS
HACKNEY CABS
TRUNDLE!
GASP! TAXIS! 'COS WHEN YOU'RE SPOTTY LIKE ME EVERYBODY CRACKS JOKES ABOUT ACNE CABS.
FLING!
ROOM 101
TRING!
TRING!
THE SCHOOL BELL! IT ALWAYS GOES OFF IN THE MORNING AGES BEFORE I GET TO SCHOOL.
ROOM 101
GRR! I'D THROW A TANTRUM – I CAN'T STAND CLUTTER AND ROOM 101 IS NOW A BLOOMIN' TIP!
STOMP!
STOMP!
HACKNEY CABS

BASH STREET GHOSTS
Reader's voice.
HMM! WHY ARE THE KIDS SO QUIET?
TIP TOE
TIP TOE
HUSH-A BYE TEACHER READING THE NEWS SHUT BOTH YOUR EYES AND HAVE A NICE SNOOZE!
SSSH!
ZZZZ! SNORE!
WHEW! A BAD DREAM! I'LL WAKEN SOON!
WOBBLE
SHAKE
GLOOP
EH? WHAT'S THAT NOISE? SOUNDS LIKE A SWAMP!
OOH! I'D BETTER WATCH WHERE I'M WALKING!
GURGLE
CHIPS
Meanwhile —
JANITOR! WHERE ARE YOU? I HAVE A LIST OF JOBS FOR YOU! JANITOR!
HOI! HUSH!
JANITOR!
LET'S KEEP OUT OF THAT OLD MOANER'S WAY!
BRUSH WEEKLY
FISH WEEKLY
CELLAR
WHAT'S GOING ON?
LIFT
FISH WEEKLY
EH? I'M NOT ASLEEP!

WE HAVE A SURPRISE FOR TEACHER DOWN BELOW!
'BYE!
DROP
ZZZZ! SNORE!
WHISPER! TORCHES ON, PALS!
EH? WHERE AM I?
CLICK!
CLICK!
EEK! A NIGHTMARE! OOOO! HORRIBLE!
OOOBLE!
CLICK!
GET READY WITH THE . . .
WAA! WHERE AM I?
. . . WET PANCAKES! HO-HO!
YEEEAAGH!
GIBBER! BE GONE, SPOOKS!
CHORTLE! TEACHER WILL NEED A WEEK OFF SCHOOL TO RECOVER!
In the Head's study —
RANT! SCARED ME HALF TO DEATH! IT WAS HORRIBLE! PUNISH THEM, HEADMASTER!
HMM!
I HAVE JUST THE PUNISHMENT TO FIT THE CRIME!
Later —
GHOST WALK 50P
PLOP!
CLICK!
TITTER! HEAD'S MAKING THEM WORK THEIR 'GHOST TRICK' FOR A YEAR'S SUPPLY OF BISCUITS FOR THE STAFF ROOM! HA-HA!
EEK!
WAH!
CLICK!

HEAT RAVE
SLURP!
GASP! WHAT A HEAT TODAY!
FLOP
FAN
YUM!
SIZZLE!
HA-HA! COOL OUTFIT!
CHORTLE!
HUH! SIT DOWN! THERE'S WORK TO BE DONE!
Then —
HOI! DELIVERY OF ICE!
EH?
IN HERE, MISTER!
YEAH!
OKAY!
WAHEY!
COOL!
COLD AIR
ICY BLAST
HMM! I'LL FIX YOU UP WITH A COOLING FAN, TEACHER!
ICE
PHEW! GREAT!
COLD WATER
ICE
WHIRL
LOVELY COOL AIR
THANK YOU, JANITOR!
THAT'S OKAY!
ICE
WHIRRR
NICE BREEZE
LEAP
EXAM
I WONDER HOW THE PROPELLOR WORKS?
LET'S FIND OUT!

WE'D BETTER MOVE OUTSIDE!
ZOOM
II
OUTSIDE?
OH, NO! I REMEMBER WHAT HAPPENED LAST TIME WE MOVED OUTSIDE!
ZOOM
ZOOM
THE FIRST TIME MY BACK WAS TURNED — YOU LOT WERE OFF!
YOU'LL JUST HAVE TO COOL OFF IN HERE!
II
HUH!
AW!
Soon —
HMM! SOME OF THE ICE IS MELTING ALREADY!
GAG!
FISHY NIFF
WHEW!
MELT!
FISHY
PONG
MELT!
THIS SHOULD HAVE COME TO THE KITCHEN! I'M MAKING FISH AND PRUNE PIE!
GROO!
SIR! IT'S GETTING HOT AGAIN!
BANG!
I'LL SEND FOR THE JANITOR! HE'LL COOL THE ROOM DOWN!
SPIN
GASP!
IT'S NOT FAIR! WE'LL FIX IT!
Later.
SPIN
BLAST OF AIR
BLAST
Suddenly.
WHEEEEEE
WHOOSH
RRIP
WHIRRRRR
GASP!
IT'S A COOL CLASS NOW, TEACHER!
WHIRRRRRRR
HO-HO! AN OPEN-TOPPED ROOM!

VOTE VOTE VOTE
FUN
DON'T EXPECT THE KIDS WILL BE INTERESTED IN THE ELECTION FOR CLASS LEADER I ORGANISED.
VOTE FOR ME!
VOTE FOR FATTY
RAZZ TO HIM — VOTE FOR ME!
VOTE FOR PLUG
NO, ME!
IT'S GOT TO BE SMIFFY
VOTE FOR SIDNEY
VOTE FOR SPOTTY
GIBBER! I DO BELIEVE THEY ARE KEEN ON THE IDEA.
IIB
STAGGER
CHOMP! GUZZLE!
DISGUSTING GLUTTONY!
VOTE FOR TOOTS!
OOPS!
I'VE HAD ENOUGH! I'M OFF TO THE STAFF ROOM FOR TEA. YOU ELECT A CLASSROOM LEADER WHILE I'M AWAY.
THROW
BURST OUT
VOTE FOR 'ERBERT
A cup of tea and a biccie later —
I'M BACK!
I'M THE CLASSROOM LEADER, TEACHER.
SPLENDID, DANIEL!

SPEECH TIME!
MUST TALK TO THE VOTERS!
VOTE FOR SIDNEY
IT'S SMIFFY
VOTE FOR TOOTS
VOTE FOR ME AND YOU'LL GET LOTS OF . . . MM . . . LOVELY . . . YUMMY —
FOOD HAMPER
ON SECOND THOUGHTS —
DON'T BOTHER!
VOTE FOR TOOTS AND GET FREE MEDICAL CARE!
GROAN!
MAY I PUT UP A FEW OF MY POSTERS, TEACHER?
PASTE
DOH! GO AHEAD!
But —
HOI!
DIM-EYED PEST!
DID EVERYONE TAKE PART? HOW DID THE COUNT GO?
EVERYONE TOOK PART OK . . .
. . . IN A HUGE PUNCH-UP.
. . . AND THE COUNT WENT UP TO TEN — THEY'RE ALL KNOCKED OUT.
IIB
BLITHER! DANNY WON FAIR AND SQUARE.
STAGGER
THIS IS THE WAY WE ALWAYS PICK A LEADER.

GARDENING CALENDAR
FROM THE
BASH STREET POTTING SHED
APRIL – APRIL IS THE TIME TO HANG UP A BIRD FEEDER. THE BIRDS WILL REALLY THANK YOU FOR IT.
WILFRID'S OUR BIRD FEEDER!
TUG!
HUP YOU GO!
MAY – THIS MONTH, LAWNS SHOULD BE GIVEN A LIGHT ROLLING!
HEE-HEE! I'LL SOON MAKE LIGHT WORK OF IT.
FLATTEN!
SMASH!
TRUNDLE
SQUASH!
SCHOOL PLAYING FIELD
JUNE – IT'S VERY IMPORTANT TO VENTILATE YOUR GREENHOUSE IN THE HOT GROWING SEASON.
TINKLE!
THWACK!
WHEEE!
NO PROBLEM TO US!
'COS IT'S THE TENNIS SEASON.

CELEBRITY FIT KIDS
DRING!
DRING!
WHEEZE!
SCHNORPH!
SNORE!
ZZZ!
LAZY SHOWER! IN MY DAY, WE'D BE OFF OUT TO THE PLAYGROUND LIKE A SHOT!
SCHOOL
OUT! OUT! DO SOMETHING ENERGETIC.
OKAY! WE'LL EXERCISE OUR JAWS IN THE TUCK SHOP.
SHOVE!
PUSH!
ZOOM!
TUCK SHOP
TUCK IN!
CHOCOLATE
POP
CRISPS
BURP! TIRING WORK BEING A SLOB!
BOYLP!
BELCH!
PARP!
RUBBISH BIN
PHEW! THE TUCK SHOP'S TUCKERED ME OUT.

THIS ARTICLE IS SO TRUE! THE BASH STREET KIDS ARE A BUNCH OF LARDY BOTS!
SPLUTTER!
WHAT?
MODERN KIDS ARE GETTING FATTER
STAFF ROOM
WHO ARE YOU CALLING FAT, SIR?
WE'RE WELL PADDED, THAT'S ALL!
IT'S JUST PUPPY FAT!
THUD!
THUMP!
THUD!
THUMP!
OMINOUS
CREAK!
HMM! MUST BE A MASSIVE ST BERNARD PUPPY THEN.
KERRASH!
AARGH!!
GOSH! YOU'RE TOO HEAVY FOR OUR STAFF ROOM FLOOR, THAT'S FOR SURE!
AAH! I'VE SPOTTED THE VERY THING FOR OUR PODGY GUZZLERS.
CLICK!
CLICK!
MOBILE PHONE
MAYBE WE COULD EAT OUR WAY OUT OF HERE.
NAH! FLOORBOARDS ARE TASTELESS WITHOUT TOMATO KETCHUP.
Eventually —
OUT YOU COME! I'M TAKING YOU FOR A SPECIAL TREAT.
SLOBBER! IS IT A FOOD FESTIVAL, SIR?
OR A PIE-EATING CONTEST?

TV STUDIOS
HERE WE ARE, KIDS. YOU'RE GOING TO BE BIG STARS.
WOW!
WE CAN HANDLE IT, SIR.
ZOOM
SCREECH TO A HALT!
OO-ER!
WELCOME TO CELEBRITY FIT CLUB, WHERE WE'LL TURN YOU INTO SMALLER STARS. JUST REMEMBER – EAT, DON'T CHEAT!
IT'S DALE WONTON! THIS'LL MEAN DIET!
AND EXERCISE!
CHUCKLE! CORRECT!
NOW WE'LL GET YOU INTO YOUR TWO TEAMS. FATTY WILL BE IN THE TEAM OF FOUR.
HO-HO! THAT'S 'COS HE'S LIKE TWO OF ANY OF US.
OKAY, TEAMS! LET'S GET YOU WEIGHED FIRST OF ALL.
I'D RATHER WADE INTO SOME SCRUMMY TUCK.

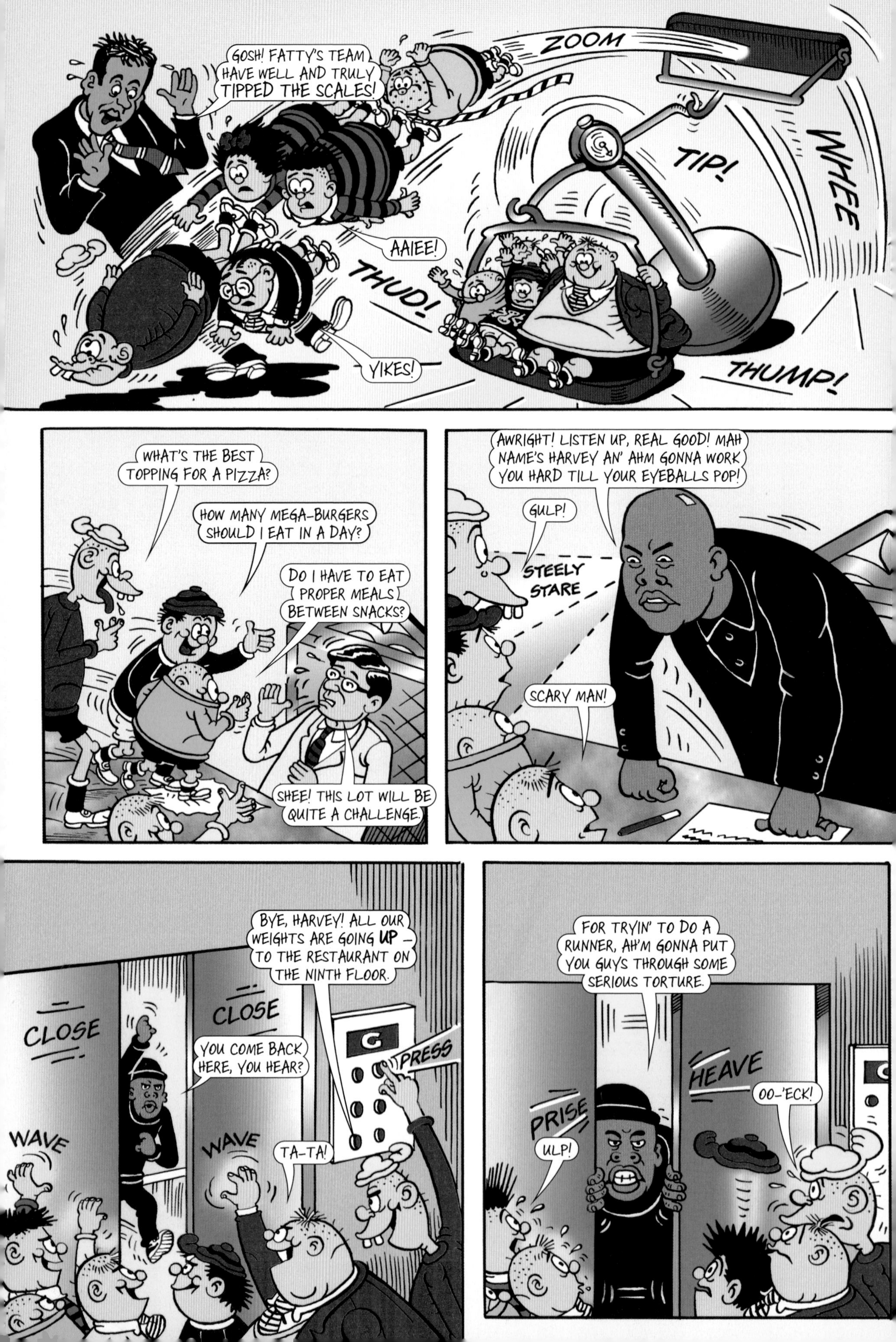
GOSH! FATTY'S TEAM HAVE WELL AND TRULY TIPPED THE SCALES!
ZOOM
WHEE
TIP!
AAIEE!
THUD!
YIKES!
THUMP!
WHAT'S THE BEST TOPPING FOR A PIZZA?
HOW MANY MEGA-BURGERS SHOULD I EAT IN A DAY?
DO I HAVE TO EAT PROPER MEALS BETWEEN SNACKS?
SHEE! THIS LOT WILL BE QUITE A CHALLENGE.
AWRIGHT! LISTEN UP, REAL GOOD! MAH NAME'S HARVEY AN' AHM GONNA WORK YOU HARD TILL YOUR EYEBALLS POP!
GULP!
STEELY STARE
SCARY MAN!
BYE, HARVEY! ALL OUR WEIGHTS ARE GOING UP – TO THE RESTAURANT ON THE NINTH FLOOR.
CLOSE
CLOSE
YOU COME BACK HERE, YOU HEAR?
G
PRESS
WAVE
WAVE
TA-TA!
FOR TRYIN' TO DO A RUNNER, AH'M GONNA PUT YOU GUYS THROUGH SOME SERIOUS TORTURE.
HEAVE
OO-'ECK!
PRISE
ULP!

HERE ARE OUR TWO EXPERTS WHO WILL ENSURE YOU ALL BECOME SLIM AND SUPERFIT.
HELLO! I'M DOCTOR ADAM WARY AND I'LL BE GIVING YOU ALL YOUR FOOD ADVICE.
A quick change later —
OKAY, MISFITS! OUTSIDE FOR A MILLION PRESS-UPS. C'MON, KEEP IT GOIN'!
SIGH! WHAT'S ALL THE RUSH?
HEE-HEE! THIS IS MY TYPE OF PRESS-UP —I'M OFF!
LIFT
PRESS!
LEAP!
Hours of training later —
WHEEZE! WE'VE MANAGED HALF A LAP.
RUNNING TRACK
LOLL
FLOP
CROAK! MY TONGUE'S HOT AS A CAMEL'S BUM.
TUG
AN' YOU OTHER BUNCHA GUTBUCKETS ARE FOR THE HIGH JUMP.
HMM!?!

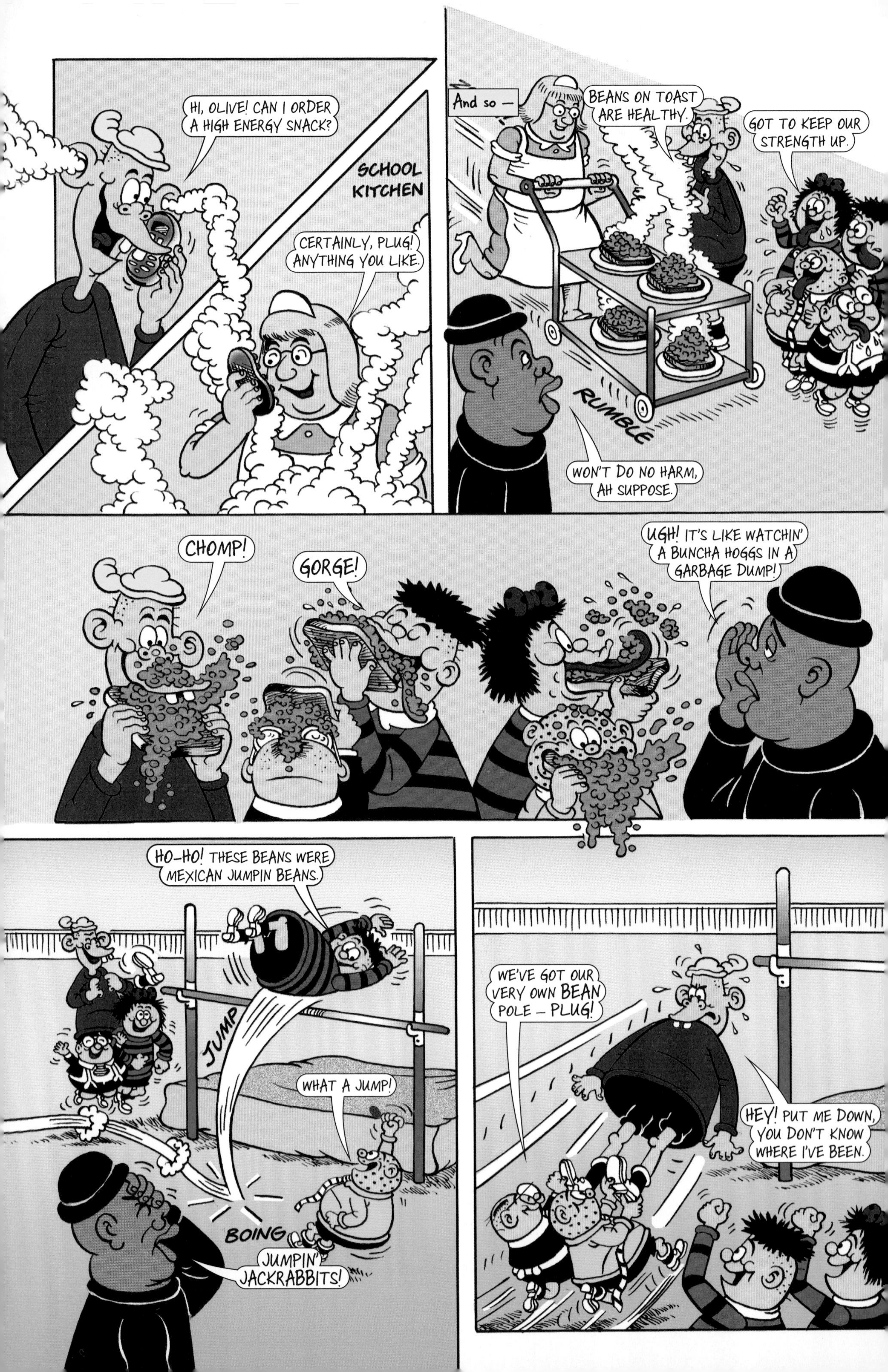
HI, OLIVE! CAN I ORDER A HIGH ENERGY SNACK?
SCHOOL KITCHEN
CERTAINLY, PLUG! ANYTHING YOU LIKE.
And so —
BEANS ON TOAST ARE HEALTHY.
GOT TO KEEP OUR STRENGTH UP.
RUMBLE
WON'T DO NO HARM, AH SUPPOSE.
CHOMP!
GORGE!
UGH! IT'S LIKE WATCHIN' A BUNCHA HOGGS IN A GARBAGE DUMP!
HO-HO! THESE BEANS WERE MEXICAN JUMPIN BEANS.
JUMP
WHAT A JUMP!
BOING
JUMPIN' JACKRABBITS!
WE'VE GOT OUR VERY OWN BEAN POLE — PLUG!
HEY! PUT ME DOWN, YOU DON'T KNOW WHERE I'VE BEEN.

WE'RE GREAT WEE CABER TOSSERS THE NOO.
WHEEEE!
TOSS!
FLING!
THESE KIDS ARE INVENTIN' THEIR OWN TRAININ'.
Ten day's physical jerks later —
RIGHT, FATTY! LET'S SEE IF YOUR FATNESS HAS TURNED INTO FITNESS. STEP ON THE SCALES, PLEASE.
OKAY, DOC!
PODDING!
PYOING
WHEE!
BUT I DID, DOC. I KEPT SAYIN' NO TO MY FAVOURITE FOOD.
CHOMP
GUZZLE
FATTY! YOU'VE PUT ON THREE STONES — YOU CAN'T HAVE BEEN FOLLOWING MY ADVICE AT ALL.
FATTY! YOUR TARGET WEIGHT LOSS FOR THE NEXT TWO WEEKS IS SEVEN STONES.
WAG
OO-ER! YES, DOC.
WE'RE ALL BEHIND YOU, FATTY. BUT REMEMBER — EAT, DON'T CHEAT!
OH, NO, DALE.
Fatty's all behind himself.

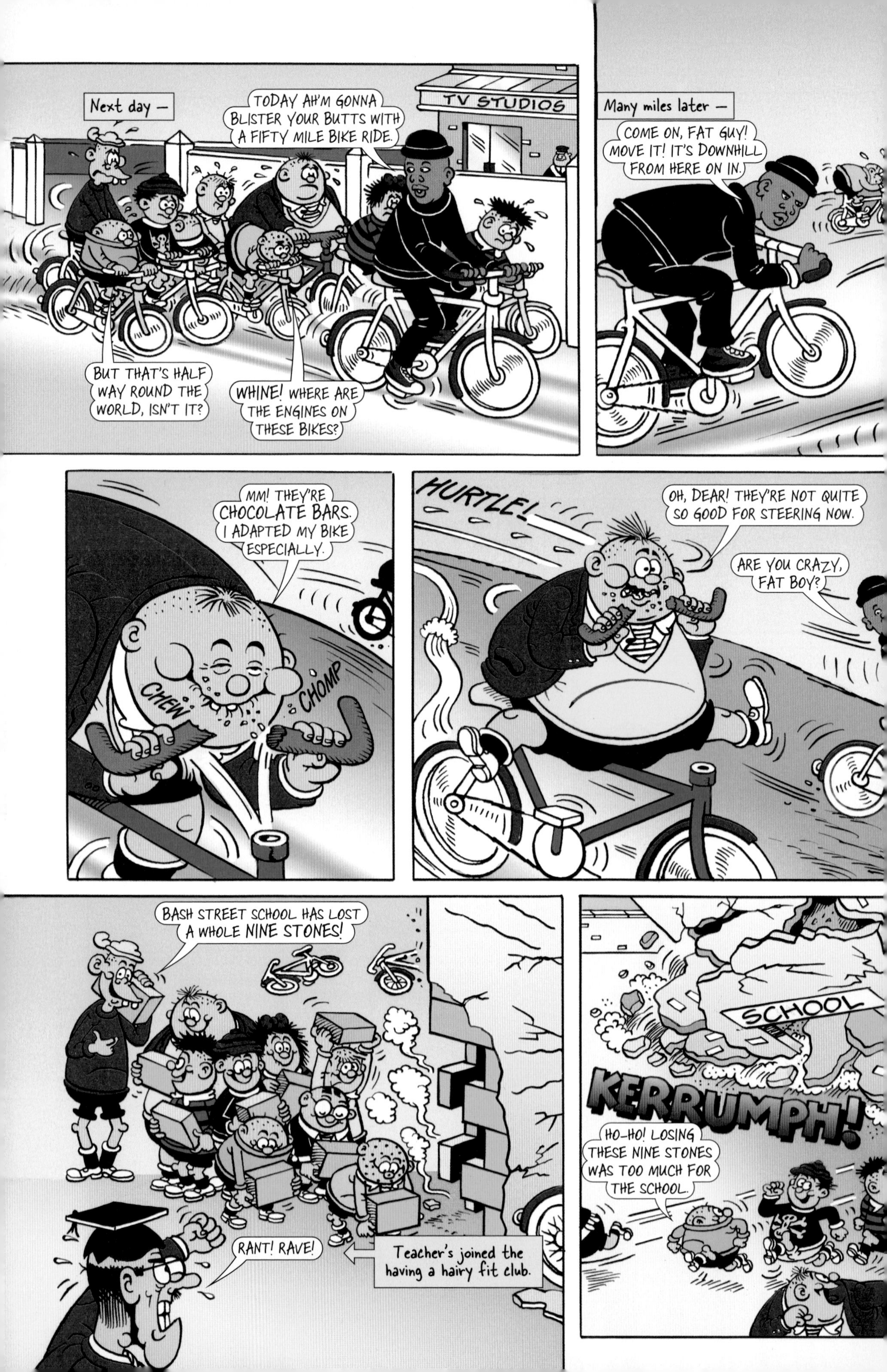

Next day —
TODAY AH'M GONNA BLISTER YOUR BUTTS WITH A FIFTY MILE BIKE RIDE.
TV STUDIOS
BUT THAT'S HALF WAY ROUND THE WORLD, ISN'T IT?
WHINE! WHERE ARE THE ENGINES ON THESE BIKES?
Many miles later —
COME ON, FAT GUY! MOVE IT! IT'S DOWNHILL FROM HERE ON IN.
MM! THEY'RE CHOCOLATE BARS. I ADAPTED MY BIKE ESPECIALLY.
CHEW
CHOMP
HURTLE!
OH, DEAR! THEY'RE NOT QUITE SO GOOD FOR STEERING NOW.
ARE YOU CRAZY, FAT BOY?
BASH STREET SCHOOL HAS LOST A WHOLE NINE STONES!
RANT! RAVE!
Teacher's joined the having a hairy fit club.
SCHOOL
KERRUMPH!
HO-HO! LOSING THESE NINE STONES WAS TOO MUCH FOR THE SCHOOL.

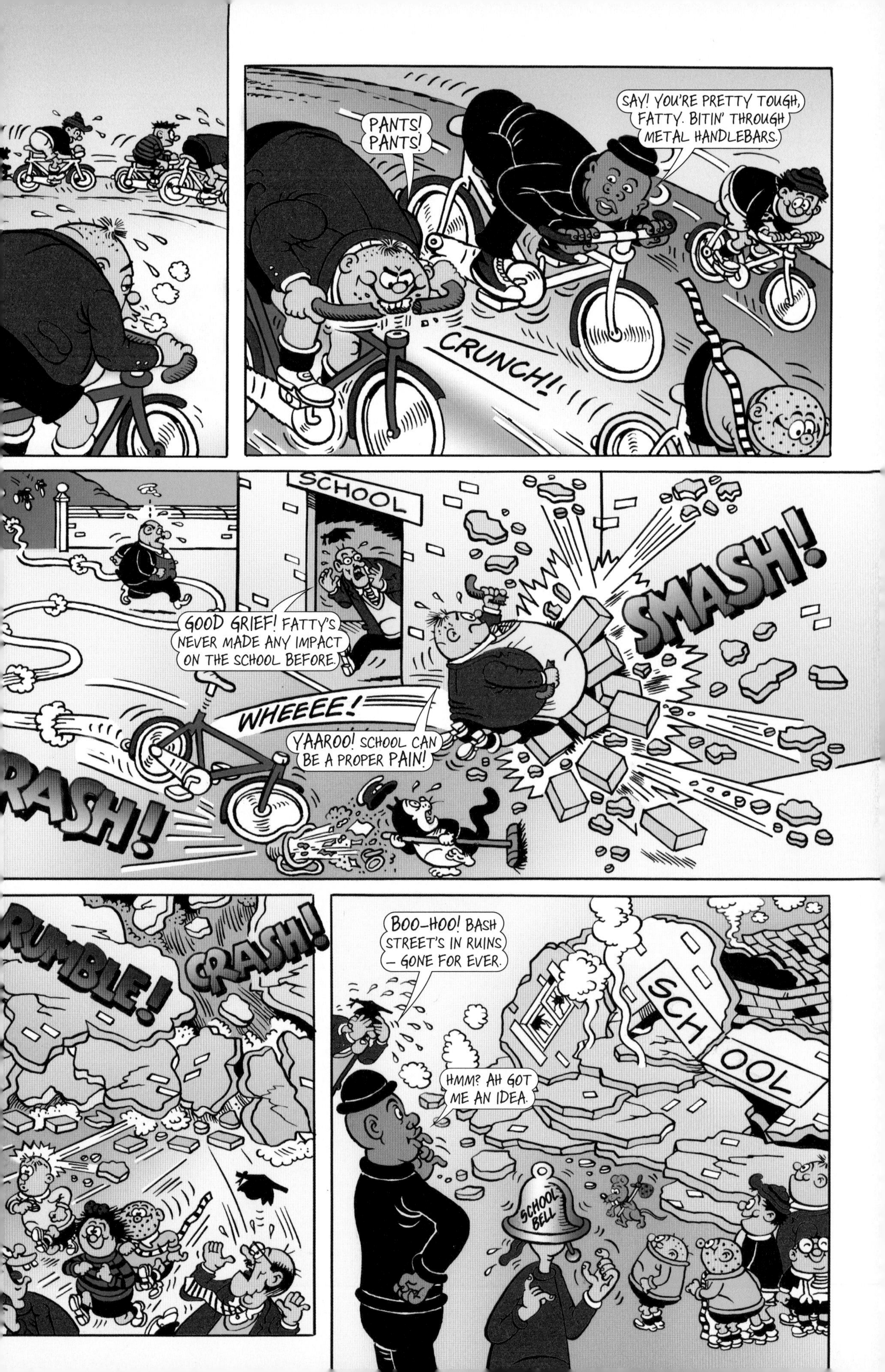

PANTS! PANTS!
SAY! YOU'RE PRETTY TOUGH, FATTY. BITIN' THROUGH METAL HANDLEBARS.
CRUNCH!
SCHOOL
GOOD GRIEF! FATTY'S NEVER MADE ANY IMPACT ON THE SCHOOL BEFORE.
SMASH!
WHEEEE!
YAAROO! SCHOOL CAN BE A PROPER PAIN!
RASH!
RUMBLE!
CRASH!
BOO-HOO! BASH STREET'S IN RUINS – GONE FOR EVER.
SCH OOL
HMM? AH GOT ME AN IDEA.
SCHOOL BELL

And —
COME ON — KEEP IT GOIN'!
SKULE
SLOP!
CHIP!
CHIP!
DAB!
GASP! WE'RE PILING ALL THESE STONES BACK ON BASH STREET SCHOOL.
PUFFITY-PUFF!
PHEW! WE'RE BOUND TO LOSE WEIGHT NOW.
SWOOSH!
SAND
CEMENT
EMENT
DS
HEE-HEE! THE KIDS SEEM TO HAVE QUITE AN APPETITE FOR HARD WORK AT LAST.

LITTLE MONSTERS OF ROCK
TWANG!
TWANG!
PLONK!
PLUNK!
It's the kids' weekly music class —
THUD!
WHEE
WHEE
PAARP!
GENTLE TINKLINGS!
STOMP!
THUD!
PARP!
SPLASH!
THUD!
TWANG!
CLICK
CLACK
QUIET! YOU LOT WILL NEVER MAKE PROPER MUSIC.
WHAT AN INCREDIBLY UNRULY CLASS.
SLAM SHUT!
POUR
DRIP

HI! I'M FROM CHANNEL 4½ TV – WE'D LIKE TO DO A SERIES, FEATURING YOUR MUSIC CLASS HERE.
MUSIC ROOM
WHAT? THIS SHOWER CAN'T EVEN SPELL MUSIC!
OUR TALENTS HAVE BEEN RECOGNISED AT LAST.
CHILD GENIUSES, WE ARE!
IT'S A FLY-ON-THE-WALL DOCUMENTARY ABOUT YOUR CLASS LEARNING TO BE STAR MUSICIANS.
SPLUTTER! I'M A TEACHER, NOT A MIRACLE WORKER.
A FLY ON THE WALL. IT'S GONNA FACE THE MUSIC.
WHAP!
MISSED!
BZZZ!
DON'T WORRY, SIR. WE SUPPLY A VERY SPECIAL TEACHER . . .
VAROOM
BLAST OF ROCK MUSIC!
PURRRR
. . . GENE STRUMMONS, SUPERSTAR GUITARIST WITH AMERICAN HEAVY METAL BAND, SNOG!
NONE THE WISER
HOWDY, Y'ALL!
COOL!
WICKED!
OKAY, KIDS! AH'M GONNA TURN OF YOU INTO A FULL BLOWN HEAVY ROCK BAND. AWRIGHT?
COR, YEAH! WE'RE UP FOR IT, MR STRUMMONS.

OKAY, NOW WHO'S GONNA BE OUR LEAD SINGER?
TAP!
TAP!
LET'S SEE WHAT'S GOING ON HERE, DASHER.
SCREAM. KEEP IT AWAY FROM MEEEE!!!
TUG!
SCREAM!
HEY! THAT'S A POWERFUL VOICE, TOOTS – YOU'VE GOT THE GIG.
I'M STARVIN'! WHEN DO WE GET A BREAK FOR GRUB?
BOOM!
BOOM!
AH'VE GOT A GUT FEELING YOU'LL BE OUR DRUMMER, FATTY.
NOW, LEAD GUITAR – YOU LOOK THE PART, YOUNG MAN.
ME, SIR? BUT AREN'T ROCK GUITARISTS SOMEWHAT SCRUFFY?
YEAH! BUT NOT ANGUS YOUNG OF AC/DC. HE LOOKS LIKE YOU.
LIFT!
PLOP!
OH, DEAR! WHATEVER WOULD MUMSIE SAY?

YOU, PLUG, HAVE JUST GOTTA BE OUR STAR BASS GUITARIST.
'COS OF MY HUNKY GOOD LOOKS THAT'LL DRIVE THE GIRLS WILD, EH?
NO, 'COS YOU'RE THE ONLY ONE WITH LONG ENOUGH ARMS TO PLAY IT.
SIGH! I THOUGHT AS MUCH.
PLONK
AAARGH! WE'RE ROADIES ALL RIGHT.
FATTY'S USING US AS A MAIN ROAD!
CHUCKLE!
ZOOM!
QUASH!
SQUISH!
FLATTEN!
HOWL!
RUMBLE!
Later —
PLAYING LIVE TONIGHT ~ THE MONSTER KIDS OF ROCK
WOW! SOUNDS WILD.
COULD BE THE NEW U2!
That evening —
AWRIGHT! YOU BEAUTIFUL PEOPLE. PUT YER HANDS TOGETHER FOR A FANTASTIC NEW BAND, ALL THE WAY FROM BASH STREET SCHOOL . . .

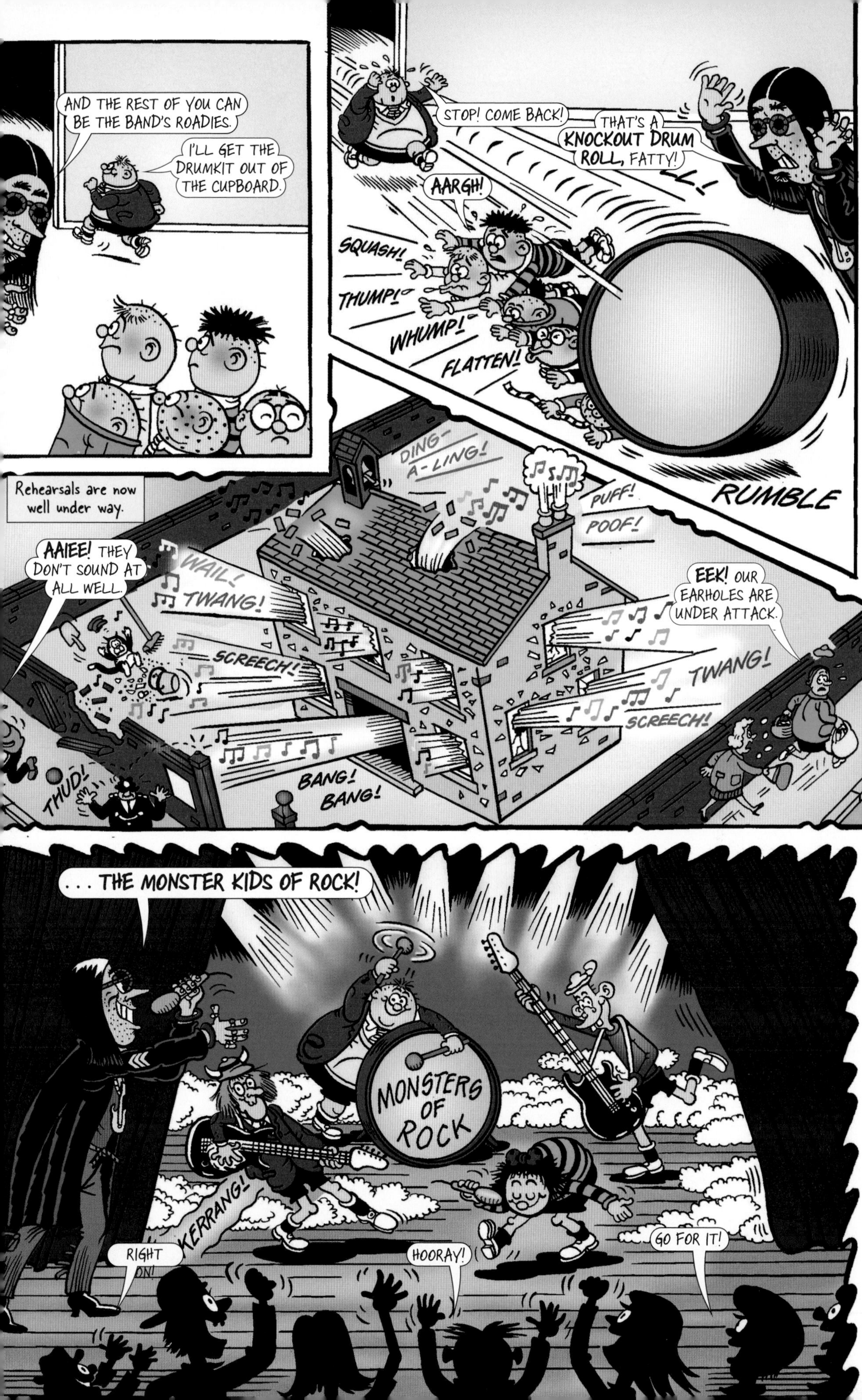

AND THE REST OF YOU CAN BE THE BAND'S ROADIES.
I'LL GET THE DRUMKIT OUT OF THE CUPBOARD.
STOP! COME BACK!
THAT'S A KNOCKOUT DRUM ROLL, FATTY!
AARGH!
SQUASH!
THUMP!
WHUMP!
FLATTEN!
RUMBLE
Rehearsals are now well under way.
DING-A-LING!
PUFF!
POOF!
AAIEE! THEY DON'T SOUND AT ALL WELL.
WAIL!
TWANG!
SCREECH!
EEK! OUR EARHOLES ARE UNDER ATTACK.
TWANG!
SCREECH!
THUD!
BANG!
BANG!
. . . THE MONSTER KIDS OF ROCK!
MONSTERS OF ROCK
KERRANG!
RIGHT ON!
HOORAY!
GO FOR IT!

♫AH'M ON THE HIGHWAY TO HELENSBURGH, HIGHWAY♫ ♫TO HELENSBURGH . . .
HEY! SOUNDS JUST LIKE AC/DC!
TWANG
KERANG!
BOOM BOOM BOOM
WOOPS! MY DRUMSTICK'S GOT STAGE FRIGHT.
ZOOM!
SLIP!
TWIRL!
SWISH
BOOM-DA-BOOM!
FATTY'S DRUMSTICK
CLICK!
WHEEEE
ZZZZ!
Seconds later —
GREEN CIRCLE CEMENT
WHIRR
BLART!
OH, NO!?!
THANK YOU, THE MONSTER KIDS OF ROCK!
HA-HA! HARDEST ROCK BAND EVER.
SOLID
CHEER
WHAT A SOLID PERFORMANCE.
CAN'T MOVE
HEE-HEE! THEY DID A GOOD QUICK SET!
POOF
SMOKE MACHINE
DS

PUP PARADE
with the BASH ST. PUPS
BONES
PEEPS
'ENRY
SNIFFY
TUBBY
SPOTTY
MANFRID
WIGGY
PUG
Tum-tee...
BUMP!
ERK!
THEN—
CRUNCH
OOYAH!
POLICE
Excuse me!
He went this way, Pups.
THUD
Look— there he is!

Give me those, Enry—
Is that you, Mother?
Forgot to clean your specs again, didn't you?
Gosh! Thanks, Bones—I THOUGHT it was a bit dim outside!

LAUGH BREEDS
DOBERMAN PINCHER
PINCH!

ON A BICYCLE MADE FOR FUN
HALT
I'M GOING TO TEST THE KIDS' CYCLING SKILLS TODAY!
PLONK!
WAA!
SPIN
BUMP!
BUMP!
ZOOM
ZOOM
YAHOO! WE'RE READY, TEACHER!
AHA! A MOUNTAIN BIKE, FATTY!
GASP! PHEW!
HUMPH! A MOUNTAIN OF GRUB ON A TRAILER BEHIND HIS BIKE!
MUNCH! CHOMP!
AFTERNOON SNACK
LOOK OUT, SIR!
EH?
CLIP BOARD
SLOO!
WHAT IS IT, DANNY?
DIVE
DIVE
DIVE
CRASH
CRASH

OOH! I'LL INSPECT YOUR BIKES FIRST!
MY BIKE CAN'T GO VERY FAST — BUT I NEVER HAVE A FLAT TYRE!
SCRAPE
GOOD IDEA, TOOTS! A GREAT ADVANTAGE TO BE ABLE TO SEE BEHIND!
EH? THEY'RE FOR ME COMBING MY HAIR!
GASP!
COMB!
SHOWING OFF A BIT, ARE WE, SIDNEY?
NO, SIR! 'ERBERT'S ASLEEP IN MY CARRIER!
OH!
WE'LL BEGIN THE ROAD SKILLS LESSON!
CLIP BOARD
WHEEE
THUD
THUNK
CRACK
ZOOM
GASP!
OOPS!
Soon —
EVEN THOUGH TEACHER'S BANDAGED AND IN PAIN . . .
. . . HE'S STILL ENJOYING HIMSELF! HA-HA!
YOU'RE SETTING A BAD EXAMPLE TO MY PUPILS, SO SHAPE UP, HEAD! LEFT TURN . . . USE YOUR HAND SIGNALS! NO . . . NO . . . NOT LIKE THAT!
OOOH!
WOBBLE
WOBBLE
HA-HA! THE HEAD'S IN TROUBLE INSTEAD OF US! MAKES A CHANGE!
CHORTLE!

BASH STREET KIDDIN'
JANITOR
WHAT TYPE OF BATTERY IS THE CAPITAL OF LIBYA?
TRIPLE A.
WHAT DO YOU CALL MAGIC TABLE CANDLES?
CANDLEABRACADABRA!
WHO WAS HALF-ROBOT, HALF-GREEK WARRIOR?
DALEKXANDER THE GREAT!
WHAT IS COVERED IN WRAPPING PAPER AND HAS A LONG TAIL?
A CHRISTMAS PHEASANT!
BRAZILIAN COMEDIANS ARE NUTS!
YEAH! BUT THE SPANISH ARMADDER!
WHAT DO YOU GET IF YOUR AUNT FALLS ON HER HUSBAND?
A BROKEN UNCLE!

HOW DO TWIN SHIPYARD WORKERS TRAVEL?
DOUBLE DOCKER BUS!
WHAT DO YOU GET IF YOU CROSS A FLOWER WITH A LOVABLE SEA CREATURE?
A DOLPHINIUM!
WHY DOES MOTHER NATURE NOT LIKE WATER?
COS SHE MADE THE SEA AN ENEMY!
WHAT NURSERY RHYME CHARACTERS HAVE SPIKY HAIR?
JACK AND GEL!
OLIVE
HOW DO YOU MAKE A SHORT PERSON TALLER?
A JACK-IN-THE-SOX.
WHAT WOULD YOU FIND ON THE SEA BOTTOM?
CORAL BRIEFS!

CONNIN' THE LIBRARIAN
BLEEP
THUD
BOOT
BLEEP
THE KIDS ARE GOOD AT ALL SORTS OF GAMES BUT . . .
. . . LOOK WHAT HAPPENS WHEN I GIVE THEM A BOOK TO READ!
THUD
THUD
In the library.
GOOD DAY! I . . .
. . . OOPS!
WELCOME
BUT BE QUIET
TITTER!
SCREAM!
BANG!
BOO!
YA-BOO TO YOU
SILENT FRIGHT
HUMPH!
HAR-HAR-HAR!
THUD
TAP
TAP
TAP
Later.
THAT'S IT! WE'LL ALL TAKE OUT A BOOK TO READ!
WILL IT WORK?
CARD, PLEASE!
HEALTH AND BEAUTY
WILD ANIMAL TRAINING
HISTORY OF CONTACT LENSES
INCREASE YOUR HEIGHT
SPOTS AND RASHES CURES
COOKERY BOOK
COOKERY BOOK
PUSH

ARE THE BATTERIES FLAT, SIR?
WHERE DOES IT 'SWITCH ON', SIR?
SIGH! THE ART OF READING IS ALMOST DEAD!
THIS WAY! WE'RE GOING ON A TRIP TO BEANOTOWN LIBRARY!
HEH-HEH!
CHORTLE! JUST AS WE PLANNED. ACT SILLY WITH THE BOOKS AND GET A DAY OUT OF CLASS!
BEFORE WE GO — YOU'D ALL BETTER BEHAVE, OR ELSE!
OOF!
BUMP
OW!
SUDDEN STOP
WHAT A FRIGHT
MIRTH
THIS WAY, PESTS
HO-HO!
HOI!
ZOOM
FALL OF THE ROMAN EMPIRE
THUD!
HMM! THE LIBRARY'S COMPUTER!
Suddenly —
GASP!
WAY-O! WAY-O! WARNING!
WE'RE ALL TAKING AN INTEREST IN READING NOW! HO-HO!
READ ALL ABOUT IT!
GRRR!
WHERE IS HE?
HA-HA! DID YOU DO SOMETHING WITH THAT LIBRARY COMPUTER, DANNY?
OO . . . ER!
HEE-HEE!
ME? HOW DARE YOU SUGGEST SUCH A THING? CHORTLE!
BEANOTOWN NEWS
LOCAL TEACHER HAS OVERDUE BOOKS. RECORD-1000 YEARS. INTO HIDING TO AVOID FINE OF £1,000,000

ALL THE MOOR THE MERRIER
TEACHER HAS TAKEN HIS WILD CLASS OUT ONTO EQUALLY WILD BLARTMOOR.
OO-ER! 'TIS THE DREADED BLARTMOOR MIST.
GASP! IT'S A REAL PEA-SOUPER.
AHEM! I SEEM TO HAVE BURNT THE PEA SOUP!
OWOOO!!!
CRINGE! THAT MUST BE THE CRY OF THE HORRIBLE HOUND OF THE BUSKERVILLES.
CHUCKLE! IT'S ONLY CUTHBERT – HE'S GOT A BLISTER.
WAHEY! HITCHED A RIDE ON THE BLARTMOOR WILD PONIES.
RUMBLE!
THEY'RE ALMOST AS WILD AS THE KIDS.
HERE
THERE
EVERYWHERE
STAND AND DELIVER!
COO! DICK TURPINTINE'S DETERMINED TO HAVE HIS BEANO DELIVERED.
BEANO
OUR BEANOS, YOU MEAN!
YOU CAN SOMETIMES SEE CHEDDAR GORGE FROM HERE.
NOT TODAY, SIR.

SPLUTTER! HAVE YOU TAKEN LEAVE OF YOUR SENSES, BOY?
YOU DID TELL ME TO PITCH THE TENT, SIR.
PITCH!
SCHOOL TENT
COME ALONG, KIDS. A TWENTY MILE ROUTE MARCH IS WHAT YOU NEED.
MUNCH! I PREFER A BEETROOT MARCH.
CHOMP!
MBLE!
ER, YOU KNOW YOU SAID WE WERE MILES AWAY FROM ANY TOURISTS, SIR?
YES — WE'RE COMPLETELY ALONE.
VENUS TOURS
OUT OF THIS WORLD
SMILE, PLEASE, EARTHLINGS!
CLICK!
YUM-YUM! YOU CAN SEE MY CHEDDAR GORGE RIGHT HERE.
HEW!
CHOMP!
ISN'T THIS ANCIENT STONE CIRCLE EXCITING, SIR?
I EXPECT THE ANCIENT DRUIDS BUILT IT.
HEH! WE RECKON IT WAS BUILT MUCH MORE RECENTLY, SIR.
YEAH! TO TAKE TRAFFIC TO THE WEST COUNTRY.
DS

GRIN AT THE DEEP END
GONE TO THE SWIMMING POOL, READERS
SMIFFY FORGOT TO TAKE HIS COSSIE!
At the pool.
HEH-HEH! LAST ONE IN IS A ROTTEN EGG!
BUT I ALWAYS LIKE A BIG DOUGHNUT RING AROUND ME IN CASE I FEEL HUNGRY! YUM!
HAR-HAR!
SIGH!
TUG
RIP
BITE
SIR! CAN'T I BRING MY INFLATABLE TOY INTO THE WATER?
ER . . . OKAY, DANNY!
U2
SPLASH!
SPLASH!
FAST
VERY FAST
HEH-HEH!
YAHOO!
AHA!
VERY FAST
HAR-HAR! I'LL BE IN THE POOL FIRST TO CATCH THEM!
LEAP
ZOOM
ZOOM
HMM! WHY DIDN'T THEY COME DOWN THIS FLUME?
VERY FAST
DOH!
That's why!

DIVE
OW!
CLANG
OOH!
SILLY SMIFFY!
GREAT DIVING SUIT THIS — A BIT HEAVY THOUGH!
HO-HO! WE THOUGHT HE WAS DOWN THERE!
CAN'T SWIM, EH, FATTY?
I CAN SWIM OKAY!
TOSS!
BUMP!
OOF!
GRRR! C'MERE, YOU LOT!
THUMP!
LET'S GO!
THIS WAY TO THE WATER SLIDES, KIDS!
GRRR!
WHEEE
THUD
VERY FAST
FAST
HOI!
WHEEE
HAR-HAR!
SPLASH
VERY FAST
HOI! LET ME OUT, PUPILS!
THUMP
THUD
OUT OF ORDER
HO-HO! WE'LL UNCORK TEACHER ONCE IT'S TIME TO GO HOME!
YAHOO!
BOING

H2O HO-HO-HO!
SIGN BACK THERE SAID 'DANGER'.
HUH! WHAT CAN HAPPEN TODAY?
BASH STREET SCHOOL
AAAAARGH!
BASH
HOI!
AAAGH!
ROAD
ROAD
GET OUT OF OUR HOLE!
THEY JUST NEED A FEW ALTERATIONS!
CLANG!
CLANG!
SWOOSH
PERFECT!
A SUPER SHOOTING GALLERY!
PING
TWANG
'MORNING!
'MORNING!
ROAD WORKS DIVERSION
OOPS! ROAD SIGNS!
WE MUST OBEY!
HUMPH! ANOTHER SIGN! WHAT A LONG DIVERSION!
ROAD WORKS DIVERSION

NO PLAYING IN THERE!
WAA! THE BASH STREET KIDS!
GRRR!
EEK!
HELP! MUMMY!
KEEP THEM AWAY!
ZOOM
GRR!
HMM! WATER PIPES!
JANITOR'S HOUSE
TO SCHOOL
WATER FIGHTS NOW!
SPLOOSH
SWOOSH
At Janitor's house.
TRA-LA-LA!
AAARGH! WHERE'S MY WATER SUPPLY?
HO-HO! IT'S NOT JUST THE WATER PIPES WE'VE HAD FUN WITH!
SWOOSH
PERMARKET
BARGAINS
EH?
ROAD WORKS DIVERSION
And —
ROAD WORKS DIVERSION
AAGH!
WAH!
BANG!
EEK!
ARE YOU SURE WE DIDN'T MISS ANY SIGNS, HEADMASTER?
GASP! NO!
SNORT
ROAD WORKS DIVERSION
ROAD WORKS DIVERSION
HO-HO! GUESS WHO PUT OUT THOSE SIGNS!
KEEP THEM OUT OF OUR WAY FOR AGES!

CASTAWAYS ON SILLY ISLE
WHAT SINGLE ITEM WOULD THE KIDS TAKE WITH THEM ON A DESERT ISLAND?
I'D HAVE A COOL GRASS SKIRT TO SHOW OFF MY TRIM FIGURE.
SWAY
HIS BEACH BUM LOOKS BIG IN THAT.
I'D TAKE A METAL DETECTOR IN CASE I WAS ON A TRAFFIC ISLAND AND I COULD FIND A BUS TO TAKE ME HOME.
BEEP!
BEEP!
BEEP!
I'D TAKE A BEACH BALL SO I COULD PLAY WITH THE LOCAL SEALS.
TOSS!
BOUNCE
I'D BRING A PHOTO OF MYSELF TO PUT IN A WASHED-UP BOTTLE. IT'S BOUND TO ATTRACT A BEAUTIFUL MERMAID GIRLFRIEND.
PUSH!
AAGH! IN YOUR DREAMS.

I'D TAKE A POST BOX SO I CAN WRITE HOME TO MUM.
IBBLE!
SLATE
HE'S GOT A SLATE MISSING IF HE THINKS A POSTMAN WILL COME OUT HERE TO COLLECT IT.
I'D TAKE ALONG MY LITTLE TOY BOAT TO MAKE SURE I GOT MY HOMEWORK TO TEACHER.
PUSH
HOME WORK
S S CRAWLEY
I'D TAKE A BEACH TOWEL TO RESERVE ME A SUNBATHING SPOT – BEACHES ALWAYS GET CROWDED IN SUMMER.
FLIP!
I'D BRING A STIFF, STARCHED HAMMOCK 'COS THERE'S ONLY ONE TREE TO TIE IT TO!
DS

PUP PARADE
with the BASH ST PUPS
BONES
PEEPS
'ENRY
SNIFFY
TUBBY
SPOTTY
MANFRID
WIGGY
PUG
DROOL! One bone...
... who gets it?
We'll let the readers decide. The most entertaining Pup wins the bone.
SO-
Please...please... pretty please!
GUEST READER
HO-HO! Eight out of ten for begging!
Hmm! This is all very entertaining stuff.
ENTER SILLY SNIFFY-
What's going on?
SUDDENLY-
AAARGH!
CRASH!
TRIP
ZOOM
ROLL
Chortle! Ho-ho! Sniffy's the winner- he entertains me the most! Haw-haw!
Us cats are clever, eh?
GREAT! I've always wanted a boomerang! Wheee!
GASP! What a waste!
What a twit!
LAUGH BREEDS
GERMAN SHEPHERD

GARDENING CALENDAR
FROM THE
BASH STREET POTTING SHED
JULY— ALWAYS SEE YOUR TALL PERENNIALS ARE FIRMLY STAKED.
PLUG MAKES A PERFECT STAKE.
AND A SCARY BIRD SCARER!
SWERVE!
AUGUST— REMEMBER, IT'S NOT TOO LATE TO SOW SUMMER LETTUCE.
HO-HO! SMIFFY ALWAYS HAS US IN STITCHES.
THIS MAKES A CHANGE FROM SEWING MY SOCKS.
SEPTEMBER— AS THE SUMMER DRAWS TO A CLOSE YOU CAN START PLANTING TREES THIS MONTH.
'ERBERT! YOU'VE PLANTED THAT TREE UPSIDE DOWN.
OF COURSE! IT'S AN AUSTRALIAN EUCALYPTUS!
PUSH!

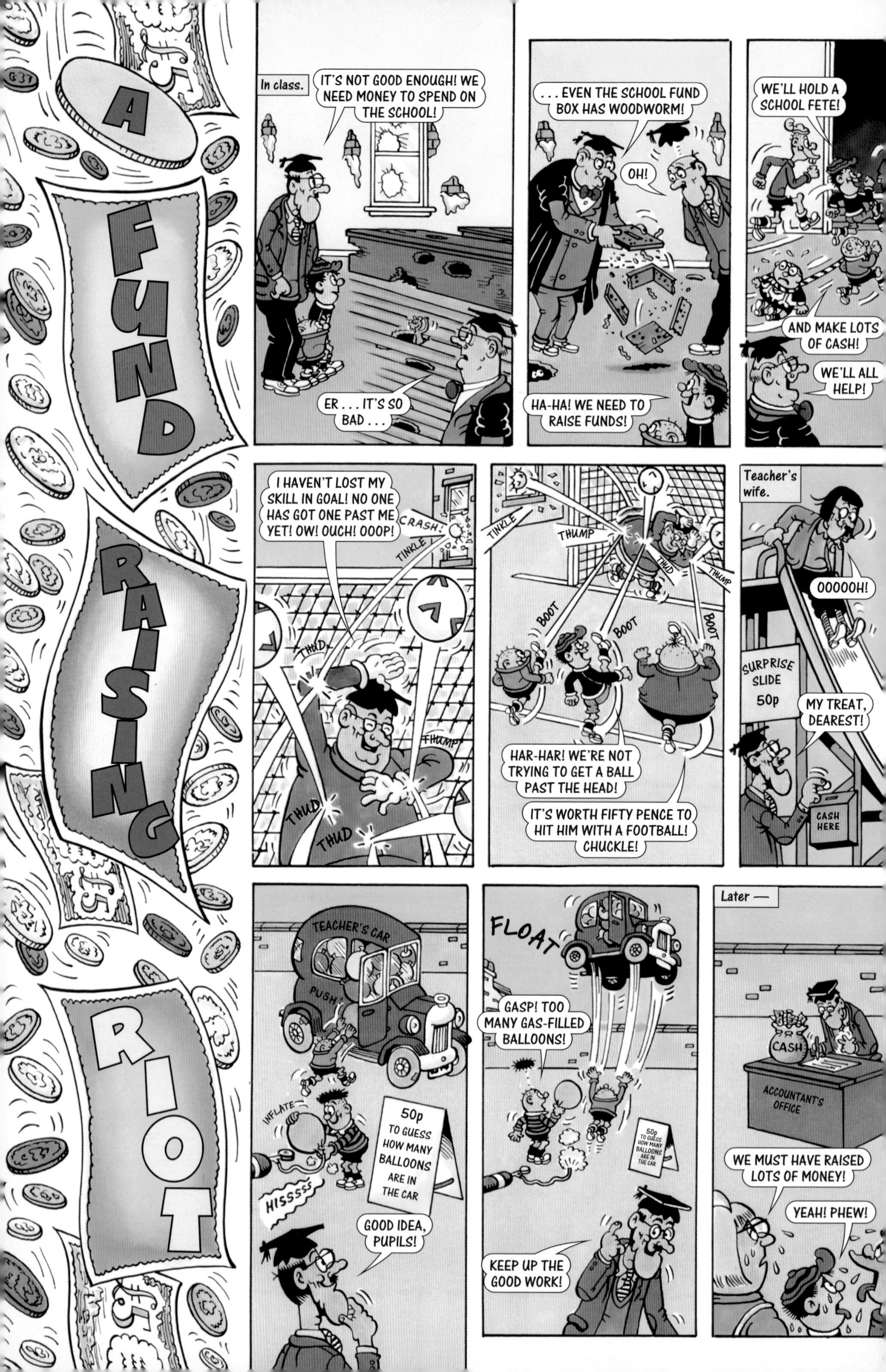

A FUND RAISING RIOT
In class.
IT'S NOT GOOD ENOUGH! WE NEED MONEY TO SPEND ON THE SCHOOL!
ER . . . IT'S SO BAD . . .
. . . EVEN THE SCHOOL FUND BOX HAS WOODWORM!
OH!
HA-HA! WE NEED TO RAISE FUNDS!
WE'LL HOLD A SCHOOL FETE!
AND MAKE LOTS OF CASH!
WE'LL ALL HELP!
I HAVEN'T LOST MY SKILL IN GOAL! NO ONE HAS GOT ONE PAST ME YET! OW! OUCH! OOOP!
CRASH!
TINKLE
THUD
THUMP
THUD
THUD
TINKLE
THUMP
THUD
THUMP
BOOT
BOOT
BOOT
HAR-HAR! WE'RE NOT TRYING TO GET A BALL PAST THE HEAD!
IT'S WORTH FIFTY PENCE TO HIT HIM WITH A FOOTBALL! CHUCKLE!
Teacher's wife.
OOOOOH!
SURPRISE SLIDE 50p
MY TREAT, DEAREST!
CASH HERE
TEACHER'S CAR
PUSH!
INFLATE
HISSSSS
50p TO GUESS HOW MANY BALLOONS ARE IN THE CAR
GOOD IDEA, PUPILS!
FLOAT
GASP! TOO MANY GAS-FILLED BALLOONS!
50p TO GUESS HOW MANY BALLOONS ARE IN THE CAR
KEEP UP THE GOOD WORK!
Later —
CASH
ACCOUNTANT'S OFFICE
WE MUST HAVE RAISED LOTS OF MONEY!
YEAH! PHEW!

Soon —
I MUST SEE WHAT FUND RAISING IDEAS THE KIDS HAVE COME UP WITH!
TUM . . . TEE . . . TUM!
WET SPONGE THROWING £100 IF YOU ARE ON TARGET
GASP! WE DON'T HAVE THAT SORT OF CASH, TOOTS!
WE'LL NEVER NEED IT — LOOK!
I COULDN'T LOOK — EVEN FOR £1,000,000!
HO-HO! SUPER IDEA!
Next —
BEAT THE GOALIE 50p
I USED TO BE RATHER GOOD IN GOALS!
THUMP
WHACK
THUD
OW! OUCH!
BOOT
BOOT
BOOT
HUH! BUT WHERE'S THE SURPRISE?
SLIDE
AAAAGH!
FISH HEAD AND PRUNE CUSTARD
SURPRISE!
ER . . . SO SORRY!
GRR! YOU SHALL BE!
I'LL BUY ALL OF YOUR SPONGE CAKES, OLIVE!
SUPER!
OLIVE
SPONGE CAKES
HOME PRODUCE
FREE!
WE'VE RUN OUT OF WOODEN BALLS TO THROW AT THE COCONUTS! HA-HA!
CRACK A COCONUT — 50p
CRACK
WOW! THEY'RE GREAT, SMIFFY!
WE HAVE RAISED LOTS OF MONEY BUT . . .
CASH
. . . WE HAVE TO TAKE OFF THE COST OF REPAIRS TO THE SCHOOL CAUSED BY FLYING FOOTBALLS AND OLIVE'S SPONGE CAKES HITTING THE WALLS!
BUT THE GOOD NEWS IS THAT WE WERE ABLE TO BUY SOMETHING NEW FOR THE SCHOOL!
YES? WHAT?
A BRAND NEW WOODEN BOX FOR HOLDING SCHOOL FUNDS — IF WE HAD ANY! AHEM!
SCHOOL FUNDS
GASP!
GRRR! SNARL!

BARRING
NNGH!
WE'RE STUCK!
HELP!
WHAT'LL WE DO, HEADMASTER? THEY'RE STUCK!
HMM! LET'S . . .
. . . PARTY!
RAZZ
YAHOO!
ONLY ONE WAY TO STOP THIS!
WE WANT OUT! WE WANT OUT! WE WANT OUT!
GRR!
OOOWP!
BOOT
A NEW PLAN — CALL THE FIRE BRIGADE!
MEE-MAW! MEE-MAW!
ZOOM
FIRE
GOOD!
CHIEF
BUMP
WHAT'S THE PROBLEM!
THAT'S MY UNCLE!
OH, NO!
CHIEF
YOU'LL NEED EXTRA FOR THESE EARS, LAD!
SLAP
SLOP
SLIP! POP! POP! SLIP! POP!
WHEW! FREE AT LAST!
MEE-MAW! MEE-MAW!
SIGH! PITY WE COULDN'T HAVE KEPT THE KIDS IN THERE FOR A BIT LONGER.
ZOOM
WAHEY!
BACK TO NORMAL!

CCIDENTS!
BETTER FREE THEM, JANITOR!
OO . . . THEY'LL NOT STOP TILL THEY'RE FREE!
AW! DO I HAVE TO?
YES!
'ULP!
HO-HO!
BZZZ
HUH! MY SAW'S BEEN BLUNT SINCE I CUT ONE OF OLIVE'S SPONGE CAKES!
WHAT?
BENT
PHEW!
LOOK! THE KIDS ARE STUCK IN THE RAILINGS! WE NEED TO FREE THEM!
HMM! NOW I SEE! I COULD USE MY SUPER CHAINSAW!
NO . . .
OR I COULD USE 'THE SLIPPERY STUFF'!
THE SLIPPERY STUFF?
BAH!
WHEEE
SLIP
GRAB
IT'S SO SLIPPERY — NO ONE CAN CARRY IT! CHORTLE!
YAROOPS!
EEK!
SLIP
WOW!
OH!
YIKES!
PLONK
CLONK
HO-HO!
OOH! RING THE FIRE BRIGADE!
PLEASE HURRY!
WE'RE TOO BUSY PLAYING FOOTBALL!
AND FINISHING A SNACK!
CHOMP! WE'LL BE TOO BUSY TO PHONE FOR AGES YET! MUNCH!

BASH STREET KIDDIN'
FATTY! WHAT CAME AFTER THE ICE AGE?
ER, THE SAUS-AGE, SIR!
WHAT WARNING SIGN WOULD YOU STICK ON FATTY?
HAZARDOUS WAIST!
WHAT FIZZES WHEN IT'S BETWEEN TWO WORDS?
A SODA HYPHEN!
WHAT'S DAFT TO PUT AT THE END OF A SENTENCE?
A FOOL STOP!
OLIVE
WHICH GAME SHOW HOST HAS EIGHT HAIRY LEGS?
CHRIS TARRANTULA!
WHAT DOES A VERY SERIOUS PERSON WEAR TO BED?
A SEVERE DRESSING GOWN!

WHERE DO BIG CATS GO FOR A DRINK?
THE LION'S MAIN!
HOW WOULD YOU CLIMB ONTO A GIANT'S HEAD?
HE'D NEED A FACE LIFT!
WHAT'S GREEN AND IS UNDER A SPELL?
A TRANCE PLANT!
WHAT DID THE BEETLE SAY AFTER IT CHEWED THROUGH THE CARPET?
LINOLYUMYUM!
We ♡ the Beano
WHO LAUGHS AND RIDES A CHARIOT?
BEN HUR-HUR-HUR!
WHAT IS THE BIGGEST SCAREDY IN SCOTLAND?
BEN NERVOUS?

BANKY PANKY
I'VE JUST HEARD THAT THE SCHOOL GOVERNOR IS VISITING US THIS AFTERNOON! TAKE THE KIDS INTO TOWN AND SMARTEN THEM UP! BUY THEM SCHOOL UNIFORMS!
ER . . .
SCHOOL FUNDS
In town.
HA-HA! THIS PLAC WILL DO!
HMM! IT LOOKS EXPENSIVE!
HMM! THERE ISN'T A PENNY IN THE PIGGYBANK — HOW CAN WE BUY UNIFORMS?
HOLLOW OINK
I'LL BUY THE PIGGYBANK FROM YOU!
EH?
HEH-HEH!
OINKY-OINK!
PORKY HERE WAS NEEDING COMPANY!
Then, at the market.
WE'LL GET SOMETHING CHEAP HERE!
I SAY!
ATTENTION!
The school governor is ex-army!
WOW!
LEAP
BY THE LEFT, QUICK MARCH! LEFT-LEFT-LEFT, RIGHT LEFT . . .
OO . . . ER! WHERE ARE WE GOING?
STAMP
STAMP

TAILORS SHOP
YAHOO!
SWING
TURN
I'D BETTER SEE HOW MUCH I HAVE TO SPEND!
YUM! YUM! WE'RE HUNGRY!
SLURP!
SHAKE
MOTHS
CHEW
CHOMP
CHOMP
CHEW
ER . . . WE MUST GO NOW, KIDS. NOTHING FOR US HERE!
CHORTLE!
EIGHT UNIFORMS AND ONE TENT!
BUT I DON'T NEED A TENT!
FATTY DOES! HO-HO!
HUH! THE ONLY THING THAT WOULD FIT!
HA-HA! VERY SMART!
EX SAS TENT
Back at school.
OO . . . ER! THE GOVERNOR'S HERE ALREADY!
SCHOOL GOVERNOR
CHORTLE!
HA-HA! HE'LL MARCH THEM FOR MILES! CHORTLE!
LEFT! RIGHT!
CHORTLE! HA-HA!
LEFT TURN . . .
TONI'S FISH & CHIPS
FRYING TODAY
EH?
LEFT TURN
IS HE LOST?
I SAY! BEEN YEARS SINCE I WAS IN CHARGE OF SUCH A COMPANY! MANY THANKS! EAT UP! HAW-HAW-HAW!
CHOMP! GUZZLE!
CHEW!
FRYING TODAY
BITE . . . ONE . . . TWO . . . THREE!

GARDENING CALENDAR
FROM THE
BASH STREET POTTING SHED
OCTOBER – IN PREPARATION FOR WINTER BE SURE TO INSULATE YOUR GREENHOUSE WITH BUBBLE WRAP.
ER, MAYBE WE SHOULD'VE PUT IT ON THE INSIDE!
BUBBLE WRAP
POP!
BANG!
POP!
POP!
BANG!
BANG!
POP!
BANG!
POP!
NOVEMBER – AT THIS TIME OF THE YEAR, MAKE SURE BIRDS HAVE ACCESS TO A BATH.
THEY CAN ALL SHARE TEACHER'S.
ICY BLAST
OPEN
AARGH!?!
DS
DECEMBER – AS WINTER BITES, STORE YOUR ROOT CROPS SUCH AS CARROTS AND TURNIP.
MUNCH! I'M STORING AS MANY AS I CAN. GOT TO PUT SOME FAT ON TO SEE ME THROUGH THE WINTER.
GUZZLE!
CHEW!
TURNIPS
CARROTS

TELL ALL YOUR FRIENDS -
YOU'LL FIND THE BASH STREET KIDS EVERY WEEK IN BEANO AND IN THE MONTHLY BEANOMAX TOO!
CHOC
2abc
3def
1
4ghi
5jkl
6mno
7pqrs
8tuv
9wxyz
@

BLUE
BOTTLE
BATTLE
NNEEEOOOO!
WHAT'S THE REASON FOR THIS FIENDISH DIN?
NNEEEOP!
IT'S THE BLUE-BOTTLE WARNING SIREN!
EH?
BZZZZ
ELASTIC BANDS ARE BANNED!
YES!
SNATCH!
WE'LL FIND SOMETHING ELSE TO FIRE AT THAT BOTTLE!
ZOOM
CLASS IIB
'ULP!
THIS IS CRUELTY TO INSECTS! IT MUST STOP! WE'RE ALL GOD'S CREATURES . . . RANT!
I'LL HAVE A JAM DOUGHNUT TO PASS THE TIME WHILE TEACHER RANTS ON!
RANT! RAVE!
RANT! RAVE!
BITE
SQUISH

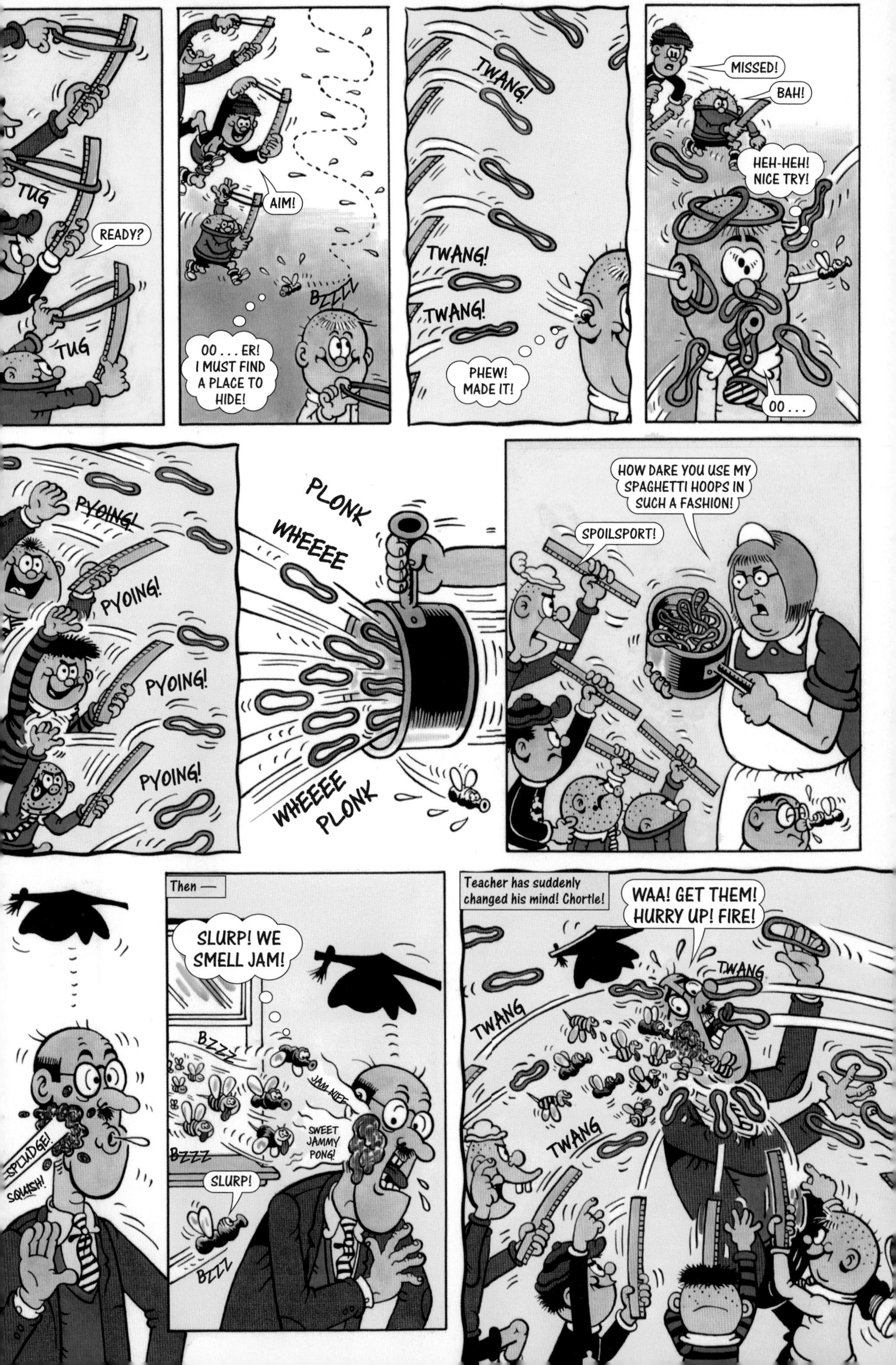
TUG
READY?
TUG
AIM!
OO . . . ER! I MUST FIND A PLACE TO HIDE!
BZZZZ
TWANG!
TWANG!
TWANG!
PHEW! MADE IT!
MISSED!
BAH!
HEH-HEH! NICE TRY!
OO . . .
PYOING!
PYOING!
PYOING!
PYOING!
PLONK
WHEEEE
WHEEEE
PLONK
HOW DARE YOU USE MY SPAGHETTI HOOPS IN SUCH A FASHION!
SPOILSPORT!
SPLUDGE!
SQUISH!
Then —
SLURP! WE SMELL JAM!
BZZZ
JAM NIFF
SWEET JAMMY PONG!
BZZZ
SLURP!
BZZZ
Teacher has suddenly changed his mind! Chortle!
WAA! GET THEM! HURRY UP! FIRE!
TWANG
TWANG
TWANG